100 *IDEAS* for *MATHS 5–7*

Dave Kirkby

Collins Educational

An Imprint of HarperCollins*Publishers*

Published by Collins Educational
An imprint of HarperCollins*Publishers* Ltd
77–85 Fulham Palace Road
Hammersmith
London
W6 8JB

© HarperCollins*Publishers* Ltd 1996

First published 1996

Reprinted 1997

ISBN 0 00 312008 2

Dave Kirkby asserts the moral right to be identified
as the author of this work.

Illustrations: Jean de Lemos, Archie Plumb, Martin Ursell

Cover design: Clive Wilson

Cover photograph: Martin Soukias

Design & computer graphics: Alex Tucker, Holbrook Design Oxford Ltd

Printed and bound: Martins the Printers Ltd, Berwick on Tweed

The author and publisher would like to thank the staff
and children of Larkrise First School, Oxford where the cover
photograph was taken.

Key to icons in text

Number   Shape, Space
            and Measures

Using and Applying Mathematics
is not identified by a separate icon
but permeates much of the work.

Contents

	Idea	Teacher's Notes			
Counting	1–3	Fruit trees	*7*	pcm 1 for ideas 1–3	11
	4–6	Birthday cakes	*8*	pcm 2 for ideas 4, 6	12
	7–9	Jars of nuts	*9*	pcm 3 for ideas 7–9	13
	10–12	Chocolate bars	*10*	pcm 4 for ideas 10, 11	14
Spots	13–14	Two dice	*15*	pcm 5 for idea 13	19
	15–17	Three dice	*16*	pcms 6 & 7 for idea 15	20, 21
	18–19	Dominoes	*16–17*	pcm 8 for ideas 18, 19	22
	20–22	Cards	*17–18*	pcm 9 for ideas 20–22	23
Blocks and towers	23–25	Two towers	*24*	pcm 10 for idea 23	27
	26–28	Three towers	*25*	pcm 11 for idea 26	28
	29–30	Strips	*25*	pcm 12 for idea 29	29
	31–33	Cuboids	*26*	pcm 13 for ideas 31, 33	30
Grids	34–36	Missing numbers	*31*	pcm 14 for ideas 34,35	35
	37–39	Number caterpillars	*31–32*	pcm 15 for idea 37	36
	40–42	Counter patterns	*32–33*	pcm 16 for ideas 40–42	37
	43–46	Elephant games	*33–34*	pcms 17 & 18 for ideas 43–45	38, 39
Time	47–49	Clock times	*40*	pcm 19 for ideas 47–49	43
	50–52	Digital clock times	*41*	pcm 20 for ideas 50–52	44
	53	Clock game	*42*	pcm 21 for idea 53	45
	54–56	Calendars	*42*	pcm 22 for ideas 54–56	46
Addition bonds	57–58	Trains and trucks	*47*	pcm 23 for ideas 57, 58	50
	59–61	Buttons	*47–48*	pcm 24 for ideas 59, 60	51
	62–64	Number mobiles	*48*	pcm 25 for ideas 62, 64	52
	65–67	More number mobiles	*49*	pcm 26 for idea 65	53
Games	68–69	Football games	*54*	pcm 27 for ideas 68, 69	57
	70–72	Fishing games	*54–55*	pcm 28 for ideas 70–72	58
	73–76	Shape games	*55*	pcm 29 for ideas 73, 74	59
	77–79	Number races	*56*	pcm 30 for ideas 77, 78	60
Targets	80–81	Hit the target	*61*	pcm 31 for idea 80	65
	82–83	Square targets	*62*	pcm 32 for idea 82	66
	84–86	Ring-a-number	*63*	pcm 33 for ideas 84, 85	67
	87–90	Two darts	*63–64*	pcm 34 for idea 87	68
Shapes	91–93	Shapes	*69*	pcm 35 for idea 91	73
	94–97	Pinboard shapes	*69–70*	pcm 36 for ideas 94, 95	74
	98–100	Symmetry	*70–71*	pcm 37 for idea 98	75
	101–103	Circle patterns	*71–72*	pcm 38 for ideas 101, 102	76
Abacus	104–106	Abacus beads	*77*	pcm 39 for ideas 104–106	79
		Abacus	*78*	pcm 40 for ideas 107–109	80

Mathematics coverage: *National Curriculum Key Stage 1* Programme of Study

	Using and Applying Mathematics	Number	Shape, Space & Measures
Counting			
Fruit trees	1a 3ac	1a 2ab 3bc 4a	
Birthday cakes	1a 3ac	1a 2ab 3bc 4a	
Jars of nuts	1a 3ac	1a 2ab 3bc 4a	
Chocolate bars	1a 2bd 4a	1a 2ac 3bc 4b	
Spots			
Two dice	1ab 2cd 3abcd 4abc	1ac 2a 3bc 4a 5ab	
Three dice	1ab 2bcd	1ac 2a 3bc 4a 5ab	
Dominoes	1ab 2bcd 3abc 4ab	1ac 2ab 3bc 4a 5ab	
Cards	1ab 2bcd 3abc 4ab	1ac 2ab 3bc 4a 5ab	
Blocks and towers			
Two towers	1ab 3ac	1c 2ab 3bc 4a	4a
Three towers	1ab 3ac	1c 2ab 3bc 4a	4a
Strips	1ab 3ac	1c 2ab 3bc 4a 5a	4a
Cuboids	1ab 3ac	1c 5a	2ab 4a
Grids			
Missing numbers	1a 3a 4ab	2ab 3a	
Number caterpillars	1a 3a 4ab	2ab 3a	
Counter patterns	1a 3a 4ab	2ab 3abc	
Elephant game	1a 2abcd 3b	3bc 5ab	
Time			
Clock times	1a		1ac 4ab
Digital clock times	1a		1ac 4ab
Clock games	1a		3b 4ab
Calendars	1a 4a	1c 3ab	1ac 4a
Addition bonds			
Trains and trucks	1a 3ab	2a 3abc 4ab	
Buttons	1a 3ab	1c 2a 3abc 4ab	
Number mobiles	1a	1c 3bc	
More number mobiles	1a 2abcd	1c 3bc	
Games			
Football games		3bc 4a	
Fishing games			1ac 4ab
Shape games	3a		1a 2bc
Number races		2ab	
Targets			
Hit the target	1a 2abcd	1ac 3bc 4a	
Square target	1a 2abcd	1ac 3bc 4a	
Ring-a-number	1a 2abcd	1ac 3bc 4a	
Two darts	1a 2abcd	1ac 3bc 4a	
Shapes			
Shapes	3a	5ab	1a 2bc
Pinboard shapes	3a	5a	1a 2bc
Symmetry	3a		1a 2ac
Circle patterns	1a 2abcd 4a	3abc	2ac
Abacus			
Abacus beads		1c 2b 3c 4a	
Abacus	1a 2abcd 4bc	1c 2b	

Mathematics coverage: *Scottish 5 – 14 Guidelines*

	Information Handling	Number, Money, Measurement	Shape, Position, Movement
Counting			
Fruit trees	collect A, organise A	range & type A, add & subtract A, B	
Birthday cakes	collect A, organise A	range & type A, add & subtract A, B	
Jars of nuts	collect A, organise A	range & type A, add & subtract A	
Chocolate bars		range & type A, B, add & subtract A, B, multiply & divide B, fractions B	
Spots			
Two dice	collect A, organise A	range & type A, add & subtract A, B, multiply A	
Three dice	collect A, B, organise A, B, display B	range & type A, add & subtract A, B	range of shapes D, E
Dominoes	collect A, B, organise A, display B	range & type A, add & subtract A, patterns & sequences B	
Cards	collect A, B, organise A, B, display B	range & type A, add & subtract A, B, patterns & sequences B	
Blocks and towers			
Two towers	collect A, organise A	range & type A, add & subtract A, B, measure A	
Three towers	collect A, organise A	range & type A, add & subtract A, B, measure A	
Strips	collect A, organise A	range & type A, add & subtract A, B, measure A	
Cuboids	collect A	range & type A, add & subtract A, B, measure A, B	range of shapes A, B
Grids			
Missing numbers		patterns & sequences A, B	
Number caterpillars		patterns & sequences A, B	
Counter patterns		multiply B, patterns & sequences A, B	
Elephant game		range & type A, add & subtract A	
Time			
Clock times		time B, C	
Digital clock times		time B, C	
Clock game		time B, C	position & movement B
Calendars	collect B	patterns & sequences B, time C	
Addition bonds			
Trains and trucks	collect A	range & type A, add & subtract A, multiply B	
		range & type A, add & subtract A, multiply B	
Buttons	collect A	range & type A, add & subtract A, multiply B	
Number mobiles		range & type A, add & subtract A, B	
More number mobiles		range & type A, add & subtract A, B	
Games			
Football games		range & type A, add & subtract A, B	
Fishing games		add & subtract A, measure B	
Shape games		range & type A	range of shapes A, D
Number races		range & type B, round numbers B	
Targets			
Hit the target		range & type A, add & subtract A, B	
Square targets	collect B	range & type A, add & subtract A, B	
Ring-a-number		range & type A, add & subtract A, B	
Two darts	collect B	range & type A, add & subtract A, B	
Shapes			
Shapes	collect B, organise A, display B		range of shapes A
Pinboard shapes			range of shapes A, D
Symmetry			symmetry B, C
Circle patterns		multiply B, patterns & sequences B, C	
Abacus			
Abacus beads		range & type B, add & subtract C	
Abacus		range & type B	

Introduction

This book is not a course, but a rich teacher resource suitable for all teachers at Key Stage 1, irrespective of the mathematics programme offered within their school. It is a collection of interesting, purposeful mathematical activities or 'ideas' for teachers to incorporate in their children's mathematics programme at Key Stage 1. Often the ideas are just starting points. Many are open ended and can be extended and made more challenging by, for example, increasing the range of numbers used.

When to use this book

Although there is undoubtedly potential within the material for short 'ten-minute' activities, the ideas should also provide a resource to help develop children's ability to 'stay with' a piece of mathematics in depth, possibly over a long period of time.

The book can be used:
- to support other work within a mathematics scheme;
- to provide units of work in their own right;
- as a source of material for differentiated activities;
- as extra supporting material, possibly for homework.

The mathematical content

The National Curriculum
The ideas span the mathematical ability and age range of most children at Key Stage 1. While there is no intention to cover the whole of the Programme of Study, there is a strong emphasis on 'Using and Applying Mathematics'. The National Curriculum Mathematics Chart on p. 4 shows National Curriculum coverage.

The Scottish 5–14 Guidelines
Similarly, The Scottish 5–14 Guidelines chart on p.5 gives some indication of curriculum coverage. The chart cannot show references to the Problem-solving and Enquiry Skills or Probability sections of the Guidelines. These areas permeate many of the ideas.

Ideas may relate clearly to one particular aspect of mathematics, or to a range of different aspects. In each set of ideas an icon highlights the main content focus.

The structure of the book

Themes and topics
The ideas in the book are grouped around ten themes which, in turn, are subdivided into related topics with a common set of purposes.

- Some themes have a mathematical context – Counting, Addition Bonds, Time.
- Some involve a particular type of activity – Games, Targets.
- Some have a common structural ingredient – Spots, Grids, Blocks and Towers.
- One has a piece of apparatus as a common link – Abacus.

Order and differentiation
The order of the themes is random. The order within the sets of ideas in a theme, however, is generally developmental, from a simple starting point to investigations and projects of some depth, thus providing differentiated activities for children of different abilities.

Photocopymasters
Most of the themes have at least four photocopy-masters (pcms), each usually linked with one of the ideas. Although the copymasters use simple language, some children will probably need a little help to get started on the activities. Suggestions for additional ideas, based on each copymaster, are outlined in the Teacher's Notes, and will therefore require teacher input.

Classroom organisation
Suggestions for class organisation are indicated by the letters G (group), P (pair), I (individual) and occasionally C (class) in the teacher's notes. There will often be a whole class stage in teaching the idea but C is not normally indicated unless there is a special reason for doing so.

Classroom equipment and materials

Mathematics should be an active, practical experience whenever possible. Many of the ideas are of this kind. The materials needed for each idea are listed in the Teacher's Notes and on the related pcms, apart from basic equipment such as rulers, pencils and rubbers which it is assumed all children will have. The range of materials is kept to a minimum, within what is commonly available in most classrooms, e.g. dice, counters, squared paper.

Fruit trees

You will need
- copies of pcm 1
- 1–6 dice
- counters (two colours)

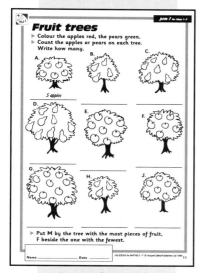

▲ *pcm 1, page 11*

Purposes
- To count up to ten.
- To count on from one number.
- To calculate one, two, three … more than a number.
- To calculate one, two, three … less than a number.
- To learn addition bonds to 10, 20.
- To recognise odd and even quantities.
- To order a set of numbers up to ten.

1 The children count the number of pieces of fruit on each tree on pcm 1 and answer the questions on the pcm.   [I | P]

Then ask:
- ▶ *Write the tree labels, in order, from fewest to most fruit.*
- ▶ *Which pear tree has most pears? Fewest pears?*
- ▶ *Which apple tree has most apples? Fewest apples?*
- ▶ *Count how many there are altogether of each fruit.*
- ▶ *How many more apples than pears are there?*

2 More activities for pcm 1:   [I | P]
- ▶ *Which trees have an odd number of pieces of fruit? Which have an even number?*
- ▶ *If each tree had three more pieces of fruit, how many would each have altogether?*
- ▶ *If two pieces of fruit were picked from each tree, how many would be left on each?*
- ▶ *Write how many more pieces of fruit need to grow on each tree to make 10 altogether, 20 altogether.*

3 **A game for two players**, using pcm 1, two dice and counters (different colour for each player). The children take turns to throw the two dice. If the pieces of fruit on a tree match the total of the two dice, they put one of their counters on a piece of fruit on the tree. The game is over when all the pieces of fruit on any one tree are covered with counters. The winner is the player who 'owns' the most trees. You 'own' a tree if you have more counters on it than your opponent.   [I | P]

Answers

1 The amount of fruit on each tree is:
A: 5 apples, B: 4 pears, C: 7 pears, D: 9 pears, E: 8 apples, F: 6 apples, G: 10 apples, H: 3 pears, I: 7 apples. G has most fruit, H fewest.
In order from fewest fruit to most they are:
H, B, A, F, C and I, E, D, G.
D has the most pears (9), H the fewest pears (3).
G has the most apples (10), A the fewest apples (5).
Altogether, there are 36 apples and 23 pears, so 13 more apples than pears.

2 The trees with an odd number of fruit are:
A, C, D, H, I.
The trees with an even number of fruit are:
B, E, F, G.
If each tree had three more pieces of fruit the totals would be:
A: 8 apples, B: 7 pears, C: 10 pears, D: 12 pears, E: 11 apples, F: 9 apples, G: 13 apples, H: 6 pears, I: 10 apples.
If two pieces were picked from each tree, the totals left would be:

A: 3 apples, B: 2 pears, C: 5 pears, D: 7 pears, E: 6 apples, F: 4 apples, G: 8 apples, H: 1 pear, I: 5 apples.
To make 10 (20) altogether each tree would need:
A: 5 (15) apples, B: 6 (16) pears, C: 3 (13) pears, D: 1 (11) pears, E: 2 (12) apples, F: 4 (14) apples, G: 0 (10) apples, H: 7 (17) pears, I: 3 (13) apples.

Birthday cakes

You will need
- copies of pcm 2
- 1–6 dice
- counters (two colours)

▲ *pcm 2, page 12*

Purposes
- To count up to 20.
- To count on from one number.
- To calculate one, two, three … more than a number.
- To calculate one, two, three … less than a number.
- To learn addition bonds to 20.
- To recognise odd and even quantities.
- To order a set of numbers up to 12.

4 The children count the candles on the birthday cakes on pcm 2, and answer the questions on the pcm. `I P`

Then ask:
- ▸ *Who is the oldest? Who is the youngest?*
- ▸ *Write the children's names in order, from youngest to oldest.*
- ▸ *Write how old the children will each be in three years' time, in five years' time, in ten years' time.*
- ▸ *Write how old the children were last year, two years ago, four years ago.*
- ▸ *Write how many years before each person is 20-years-old.*
- ▸ *Whose ages are an even number of years? Whose are an odd number of years?*

5 The children make a composite list of family, friends and pets, together with their ages. They write the names in order from youngest to oldest. They write how old each will be in a number of years' time (specify), and how old each was a number of years ago (specify). `P G`

6 A game for two players, using pcm 2, two dice and counters (different colour for each player). The children take turns to throw the two dice. If the candles on a cake match the total of the two dice, they put one of their counters on it. If the cake already has a counter, another can be placed on it. The game is over when all the cakes have at least one counter on them. The winner is the player who has 'eaten the most cakes'. You 'eat a cake' if you have more counters on it than your opponent. `P`

Answers
4 The age of each child is:
Joanne, 7; Greg, 5; Sanjit, 4; Kim, 8; Helen, 6; Fatima, 10; Ben, 12; Jed, 9; Suzi, 11.

In order from youngest to eldest they are:
Sanjit, Greg, Helen, Joanne, Kim, Jed, Fatima, Suzi, Ben.

In three (five, ten) years' time their ages will be:
Joanne, 10 (12,17);
Greg, 8 (10,15);
Sanjit, 7 (9,14),
Kim, 11 (13,18);
Helen, 9 (11,16);

Fatima, 13 (15,20);
Ben, 15 (17,22);
Jed, 12 (14,19);
Suzi, 14 (16,21).

Last year (two years, four years ago) their ages were:
Joanne, 6 (5,3);
Greg, 4 (3,1);
Sanjit, 3 (2,0);
Kim, 7 (6,4);
Helen, 5 (4,2);
Fatima, 9 (8,6);
Ben, 11 (10, 8);
Jed, 8 (7,5);
Suzi, 10 (9,7).

The number of years

before each is 20 is:
Joanne, 13;
Greg, 15;
Sanjit, 16;
Kim, 12;
Helen, 14;
Fatima, 10;
Ben, 8;
Jed, 11;
Suzi, 9.

Children whose ages are an even number of years:
Sanjit, Kim, Helen, Fatima, Ben.
Children whose ages are an odd number of years:
Joanne, Greg, Jed, Suzi.

Jars of nuts

You will need
- copies of pcm 3
- 1–6 dice
- counters (two colours)

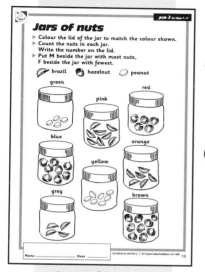

▲ *pcm 3, page 13*

Purposes
- To count up to ten.
- To count on from a number.
- To learn addition bonds to 10, 20.
- To subtract a number from ten.
- To order a set of numbers up to ten.
- To recognise odd and even quantities.

7 The children count the number of nuts in each jar on pcm 3 and answer the questions on the pcm. `I P`

Then ask:
> *How many of each type of nut are there?*
> *Which are there most of? Which are there fewest of?*

8 **i** More activities for pcm 3: `I P G`
> *Which jars have an odd number of fruit? Which have an even number?*
> *Write how many more sweets need be added to each jar to make 10 altogether, 20 altogether.*

ii The children take some jars and a collection of nuts. They place different numbers of nuts in each jar. They sort the jars according to odd and even numbers of nuts. They order them according to the numbers of nuts inside. `I P G`

9 **A game for two players**, using pcm 3, one dice and counters (different colour for each player). The children take turns to throw the dice and subtract the dice number from ten. If a jar contains a matching number of nuts, they put one of their counters on the jar. Only one counter per jar is allowed. The game is over when all the jars have a counter on them. The winner is the player who has 'eaten the most jars of nuts'. You 'eat a jar of nuts' if it contains one of your counters. `P`

Answers

7 The numbers are: green, 4; pink, 8; red, 5; blue, 8; yellow, 7; orange, 6; grey, 4; brown, 9. The brown jar has the most (9), the green and grey jars have the fewest (4). There are 18 brazils, 11 peanuts, and 22 hazelnuts.

8 The jars with an odd number of nuts are: red, yellow, brown. The jars with an even number of nuts are: green, grey, pink, blue, orange. The number needed to make each jar contain 10 (20) is: green, 6 (16); pink, 2 (12); red, 5 (15); blue, 2 (12); yellow, 3 (13); orange, 4 (14); grey, 6 (16); brown, 1 (11).

Chocolate bars

You will need
- copies of pcm 4
- square grid paper (preferably large squares, e.g. 2 cm)

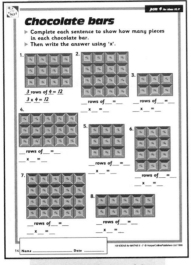

▲ pcm 4, page 14

Purposes
- To count up to 20.
- To introduce the concept of multiplication.
- To learn addition bonds to 20.
- To find one half and one quarter of a quantity.
- To divide by two and four by equal sharing.

10 The children answer the questions on pcm 4 about the number of pieces of chocolate in the bars. They record the results using 'x' notation, e.g. 3 rows of 4 = 12 can be recorded as 3 x 4 = 12. `I` `P`

Then ask:
- *Which bar has most pieces? Which fewest?*
- *How many rows in each bar? Which bars have the most rows? Which the fewest?*
- *Which bar has most pieces in each row? Which has fewest?*
- *How many pieces need to be added to each bar to make 20 pieces altogether?*

11 More questions for pcm 4: `I` `P`
- *Which bars can be shared equally between two people? Draw a line to show how the bars need to be cut to give two people equal shares.*
- *Record the results, e.g. for the first bar: '$\frac{1}{2}$ of 12 is 6'. Extend this to using '÷' notation, e.g. '12 ÷ 2 = 6'.*
- *Which bars can be shared equally between four people? Draw lines to show how the bars need to be cut to give four people equal shares.*
- *Record the results, e.g. for the first bar: '$\frac{1}{4}$ of 12 is 3'. Extend this to using '÷' notation, e.g. '12 ÷ 4 = 3'.*

12 Provide the children with squared paper (preferably large squares). Ask them to cut out some rectangles of different sizes to represent bars of chocolate. They record the number of rows, the number of pieces in each row and the total number of pieces in each bar. They investigate different ways of cutting bars of chocolate which have 12 pieces, 16 pieces. `P` `G`

Answers

10 The chocolate bars are:
1. 3 rows of 4 = 12 (3 x 4 = 12);
2. 4 rows of 4 = 16 (4 x 4 = 16).
3. 2 rows of 3 = 6 (2 x 3 = 6);
4. 3 rows of 5 = 15 (3 x 5 = 15);
5. 3 rows of 3 = 9 (3 x 3 = 9);
6. 4 rows of 3 = 12 (4 x 3 = 12);
7. 4 rows of 5 = 20 (4 x 5 = 20);
8. 2 rows of 5 = 10 (2 x 5 = 10);

The bar with the most pieces: 7, the bar with the fewest pieces: 3.
The number of rows in each bar:
1. 3   2. 4   3. 2   4. 3
5. 3   6. 4   7. 4   8. 2.
2, 6 and 7 have most rows, 3 and 8 have fewest.
The number of pieces in each row:
1. 4   2. 4   3. 3   4. 5
5. 3   6. 3   7. 5   8. 5.
To make 20 in each bar the number of pieces to be added are:
1. 8   2. 4   3. 14   4. 5
5. 11   6. 8   7. 0   8. 10.

11 The bars which can be halved are:
1. 12 ÷ 2 = 6;
2. 16 ÷ 2 = 8;
3. 6 ÷ 2 = 3;
6. 12 ÷ 2 = 6;
7. 20 ÷ 2 = 10;
8. 10 ÷ 2 = 5.
The bars which can be quartered are:
1. 12 ÷ 4 = 3;
2. 16 ÷ 4 = 4;
6. 12 ÷ 4 = 3;
7. 20 ÷ 4 = 5.

12 12 pieces can be arranged in these bars:
1 x 12, 2 x 6, 3 x 4.
16 pieces can be arranged in bars 1 x 16, 2 x 8, 4 x 4.

Fruit trees

▶ Colour the apples red, the pears green.
▶ Count the apples or pears on each tree.
  Write how many.

A.

_____5 apples_____

B.

_____

C.

_____

D.

_____

E.

_____

F.

_____

G.

_____

H.

_____

J.

_____

▶ Put **M** by the tree with the most pieces of fruit,
  F beside the one with the fewest.

Name .... Date ....

100 IDEAS for MATHS 5 –7 © HarperCollins*Publishers* Ltd 1996

Birthday cakes

▶ Count the candles on the birthday cakes.
▶ Write how old each child is.
▶ Put O by the cake for the oldest child,
  Y by the cake for the youngest.

_____   _____   _____

_____   _____   _____

_____   _____   _____

Name .... Date ....

100 IDEAS for MATHS 5–7 © HarperCollinsPublishers Ltd 1996

Jars of nuts

▶ Colour the lid of the jar to match the colour shown.
▶ Count the nuts in each jar.
  Write the number on the lid.
▶ Put **M** beside the jar with most nuts,
  F beside the jar with fewest.

 brazil   hazelnut   peanut

green

pink

red

blue

orange

yellow

grey

brown

Name .... Date ....

Chocolate bars

▶ Complete each sentence to show how many pieces in each chocolate bar.

▶ Then write the answer using 'x'.

1.

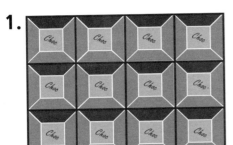

__3__ rows of __4__ = __12__

__3__ x __4__ = __12__

2.

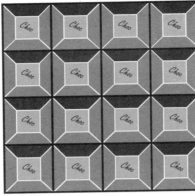

___ rows of ___ = ___

___ x ___ = ___

3.

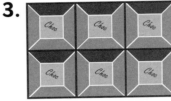

___ rows of ___ = ___

___ x ___ = ___

4.

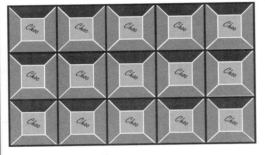

___ rows of ___ = ___

___ x ___ = ___

5.

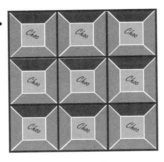

___ rows of ___ = ___

___ x ___ = ___

6.

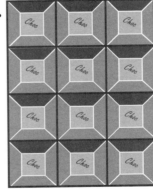

___ rows of ___ = ___

___ x ___ = ___

7.

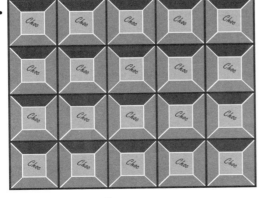

___ rows of ___ = ___

___ x ___ = ___

8.

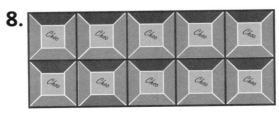

___ rows of ___ = ___

___ x ___ = ___

Name .... Date ....

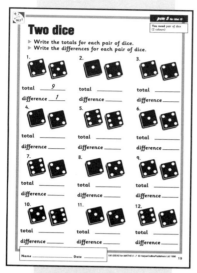

Two dice

+ x ÷ 2n ½ 963 =

You will need
- copies of pcm 5
- pairs of 1–6 dice (two colours)

▲ *pcm 5, page 19*

Purposes
- To add two single-digit numbers (total up to 20).
- To find the difference between two single-digit numbers.
- To multiply two numbers (each up to six).
- To work systematically.

13 **i** The children write the totals for each pair of dice on pcm 5. ⬚I⬚P

Then ask:

> *Investigate all the possible total scores when throwing two dice, and all the different ways of achieving each score.*

Note

The different ways of achieving each total are best shown by ensuring that the two dice are different colours, e.g. red and green.

ii They write the differences between the spots on each pair of dice on pcm 5. ⬚I⬚P

Then ask:

> *Investigate all the possible differences when throwing two dice, and all the ways of achieving each difference.*

Note

It is best to ensure that the two dice are different colours (*see above*).

iii The children multiply together the two scores on each pair of dice on pcm 5. ⬚I⬚P

14 **A game for two or more players**, using two dice. The players take turns to throw the dice and score the total. They record the scores, the winner being the first player to achieve a total of 20 points. Vary the game by scoring the difference between the two dice. ⬚P⬚G

Answers

13 **i** The totals are:
1.9 2.5 3.8 4.5 5.12
6.8 7.9 8.7 9.10 10.11
11.6 12.10.

The ways of achieving each total can be represented in an addition table. Using red and green dice:

green dice

+	1	2	3	4	5	6
1	2	3	4	5	6	7
2	3	4	5	6	7	8
3	4	5	6	7	8	9
4	5	6	7	8	9	10
5	6	7	8	9	10	11
6	7	8	9	10	11	12

red dice

ii The differences are:
1.1 2.3 3.0 4.1 5.0
6.2 7.3 8.3 9.0 10.1
11.0 12.2.

The ways of achieving each difference can be represented in a difference table. Using red and green dice:

green dice

−	1	2	3	4	5	6
1	0	1	2	3	4	5
2	1	0	1	2	3	4
3	2	1	0	1	2	3
4	3	2	1	0	1	2
5	4	3	2	1	0	1
6	5	4	3	2	1	0

red dice

iii The products are:
1.20 2.4 3.16 4.6 5.36 6.15 7.18 8.10 9.25 10.30 11.9 12.24

Three dice

Purposes

- To add three single-digit numbers (total up to 20).
- To find the difference between two single-digit numbers.
- To learn to construct a tally chart.
- To learn to construct a block graph or bar graph.
- To work systematically.

15 i The children write the totals for each set of dice on pcm 6. `I` `P` `G`

Then ask:

> ▸ *How many times does each number of spots appear on the dice on the sheet. Draw a graph to illustrate this. (The blank graphs on pcm 7 can be used for this.)*
> ▸ *Throw three dice nine times. Record the number of spots on each dice on a tally chart, then complete the chart and draw a block graph or bar graph to show the results.*

ii The children write the differences between pairs of black and white dice in the sets on pcm 6. `I` `P` `G`

16 i The children investigate all the different possible totals when throwing three dice. `P` `G`

ii They investigate different ways of achieving the same total, e.g. 13. `P` `G`

17 A **game for two or more players**, using three dice. The players take turns to throw all three dice and record the total. The winner of each round takes a counter. The winner is the one who first collects five counters. The game can be varied by adding the spots on any two dice and taking away those on the third dice. `P` `G`

You will need
- copies of pcm 6
- sets of three dice
- counters
- blank graphs on pcm 7 (optional)

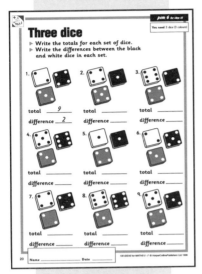

▲ pcm 6, page 20

Answers

15 **i** The totals are:

1. 9	2. 10	3. 12
4. 14	5. 6	6. 10
7. 10	8. 15	9. 12.

The number of times each number of spots appears are:

1 – 3 times	4 – 7 times
2 – 4 times	5 – 4 times
3 – 5 times	6 – 4 times.

ii The differences between black and white dice are:

1. 2	2. 3	3. 4
4. 1	5. 0	6. 3
7. 0	8. 0	9. 2.

16 **i** The different possible totals are the numbers between 3 and 18 inclusive.

ii There are five ways of achieving a total of 13: (6, 6, 1), (6, 5, 2), (6, 4, 3), (5, 5, 3), (5, 4, 4).

You will need
- copies of pcm 8
- sets of dominoes
- blank graphs on pcm 7 (optional)

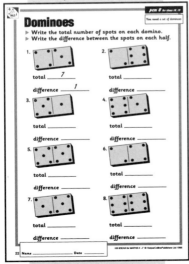

▲ pcm 8, page 22

Dominoes

Purposes

- To add two single-digit numbers (total up to 12).
- To find the difference between two single-digit numbers.
- To recognise odd and even numbers.
- To learn to construct a block graph or bar graph.

18 i The children add the spots on each half of the dominoes on pcm 8. `I` `P`

Then ask:

> ▸ *Using a complete set of dominoes, investigate the different possible totals and sort them into sets with the same total.*
> ▸ *How many are there in each set?*
> ▸ *Draw a block graph or bar graph to show the results.*

Note

There are 13 possible spot totals for the graph, ranging from 0 to 12, so 13 columns will be needed in the graph. The horizontal axis is the spot total, the vertical axis the number of dominoes. Because of the number of columns, it would be simpler for the children to construct a physical block graph on the table, using number cards to label the totals horizontally, then placing the dominoes one above the other in each category.

ii The children find the differences between the spots on each half `I` `P`
of the domino on pcm 8.

Then ask:

> ► *Using a set of dominoes, investigate the possible differences,*
> *and sort them into sets with the same difference.*
> ► *How many are there in each set?*
> ► *Draw a block graph or bar graph to show the results.*

(The blank graphs on pcm 7 can be used for this simpler graph.)

⑲ **i** The children colour the halves of each domino on pcm 8, `I` `P` `G`
the halves with an odd number of spots pink, the halves with
an even number of spots green.

Ask:

> ► *How many odd halves? How many even?*
> ► *How many dominoes have both halves the same colour?*

ii The children sort a set of dominoes (without the blanks) `I` `P` `G`
to investigate how many have both sides even, how many have
both sides odd, how many have one side even and the other odd.

Answers

⑱ **i** The totals are:
1.7   2.8   3.6   4.9   5.10   6.6   7.8   8.12.
The different possible totals, and the number of ways of making each are:

totals:	0	1	2	3	4	5	6	7	8	9	10	11	12
ways:	1	1	2	2	3	3	4	3	3	2	2	1	1

ii The differences are:
1.1   2.4   3.4   4.3   5.0   6.2   7.2   8.0.
The possible differences, and the number of ways of making each are:

differences:	0	1	2	3	4	5	6
ways:	7	6	5	4	3	2	1

⑲ The numbers are: both sides even: 6; both sides odd: 6; one side even, the other odd: 9.

Cards

Purposes

- To add two single-digit numbers (total up to 20).
- To find the difference between two single-digit numbers.
- To recognise odd and even numbers.
- To construct a block graph or bar graph.

⑳ **i** The children write the difference between the numbers of symbols `I` `P` `G`
on each pair of cards on pcm 9.

Then ask:

> ► *Use a pack of playing cards (without the picture cards), deal them out*
> *in pairs and sort the pairs according to their differences. Which pair*
> *has the smallest difference? Which has the largest difference?*
> *Which have the same difference?*
> ► *Draw a bar graph/block graph to show the difference.*
> *(The blank graphs on pcm 7 can be used for this.)*

You will need

- copies of pcm 9
- packs of playing cards
- blank graphs on pcm 7 (optional)

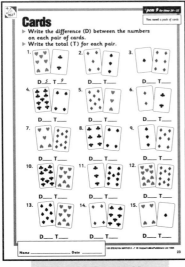

▲ *pcm 9, page 23*

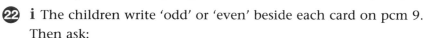
ii The children write the total number of symbols on each pair of cards on pcm 9. `I` `P` `G`

Then ask:

▸ *Use a pack of playing cards (without the picture cards), deal them out in pairs, then sort the pairs according to their totals.*
▸ *Which pair has the smallest total? Which has the largest total? Which have the same total?*
▸ *Draw a bar graph/block graph to show the totals.*

㉑ i The children use a pack of playing cards to make pairs to match each pair on pcm 9. `P` `G`

Then ask: `P` `G`

▸ *Count how many there are of each colour/suit.*
▸ *Which colour/suit has the most cards? Which has the least?*
▸ *Draw a bar graph/block graph to show the results.*
▸ *Which is the largest/smallest heart? Repeat for the other suits.*

ii The children repeat the activity by shuffling the set of cards, dealing out 15 pairs and analysing the numbers of each colour, suit, etc.

㉒ i The children write 'odd' or 'even' beside each card on pcm 9. `P` `G`

Then ask:

▸ *Count how many there are of each.*
▸ *How many pairs have both cards odd, both cards even, one of each?*

ii The children repeat the activity by shuffling the set of cards, dealing out 15 pairs and analysing the odd and even pairs. `P` `G`
They draw a block graph or bar graph to show the results.
The horizontal axis is 'odd or even', the vertical axis is 'number of cards'. There are three categories: 'both odd', 'both even', and 'one of each', so three columns will be needed. (The blank graphs on pcm 7 can be used for this.)

Answers

⑳ The differences are:

1. 5	2. 2	3. 5
4. 5	5. 5	6. 0
7. 5	8. 2	9. 4
10. 2	11. 6	12. 0
13. 0	14. 3	15. 3.

The totals are:

1. 9	2. 8	3. 7
4. 13	5. 11	6. 4
7. 15	8. 10	9. 10
10. 18	11. 12	12. 20
13. 16	14. 11	15. 5.

㉑ There are 7 hearts, 7 clubs, 8 diamonds and 8 spades, making 15 reds and 15 blacks altogether. The largest/smallest of each suit are: hearts (10, 3), clubs (10, 2), diamonds (10, 2), spades (9, 1).

㉒ 1. odd/even
2. odd/odd
3. odd/even
4. odd/even
5. even/odd
6. even/even
7. odd/even
8. even/even
9. odd/odd
10. even/even
11. odd/odd
12. even/even
13. even/even
14. even/odd
15. even/odd.
There are five pairs both even, three pairs both odd and seven pairs which have one odd and one even.

| **You need** pair of dice (2 colours) |

Two dice

▶ Write the totals for each pair of dice.
▶ Write the differences for each pair of dice.

1.

total _____ *9* _____

difference _____ *1* _____

2.

total _____

difference _____

3.

total _____

difference _____

4.

total _____

difference _____

5.

total _____

difference _____

6.

total _____

difference _____

7.

total _____

difference _____

8.

total _____

difference _____

9.

total _____

difference _____

10.

total _____

difference _____

11.

total _____

difference _____

12.

total _____

difference _____

| Name .... Date .... |

You need 3 dice (3 colours)

Three dice

▶ Write the totals for each set of dice.
▶ Write the differences between the black and white dice in each set.

1.

total _____9_____

difference _____2_____

2.

total _____

difference _____

3.
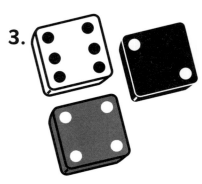

total _____

difference _____

4.

total _____

difference _____

5.

total _____

difference _____

6.

total _____

difference _____

7.

total _____

difference _____

8.

total _____

difference _____

9.

total _____

difference _____

Name .... **Date** ....

100 IDEAS for MATHS 5–7 © HarperCollins*Publishers* Ltd 1996

Block graph

totals

Bar graph

totals

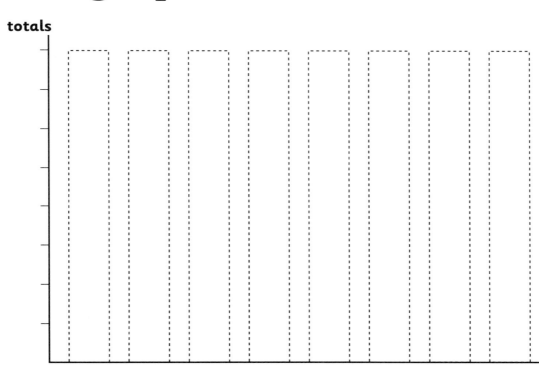

Name .... **Date** ....

You **need** a set of dominoes

Dominoes

▶ **Write the total number of spots on each domino.**
▶ **Write the difference between the spots on each half.**

1.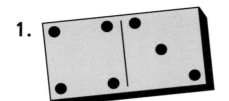

total _____7_____

difference _____1_____

2.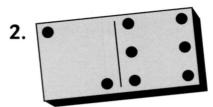

total _____

difference _____

3.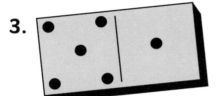

total _____

difference _____

4.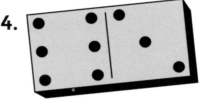

total _____

difference _____

5.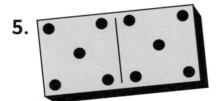

total _____

difference _____

6.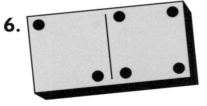

total _____

difference _____

7.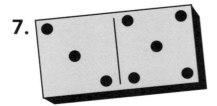

total _____

difference _____

8.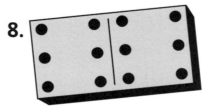

total _____

difference _____

Name .... Date ....

100 IDEAS for MATHS 5 –7 © HarperCollins*Publishers* Ltd 1996

You need a pack of cards

Cards

▶ Write the difference (D) between the numbers on each pair of cards.

▶ Write the total (T) for each pair.

1.

D _5_ T _9_

2.

D___ T___

3.

D___ T___

4.

D___ T___

5.

D___ T___

6.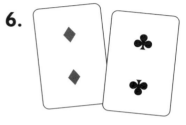

D___ T___

7.

D___ T___

8.

D___ T___

9.

D___ T___

10.

D___ T___

11.

D___ T___

12.

D___ T___

13.

D___ T___

14.

D___ T___

15.

D___ T___

100 IDEAS for MATHS 5 -7 © HarperCollins*Publishers* Ltd 1996

Name .... Date ....

Two towers

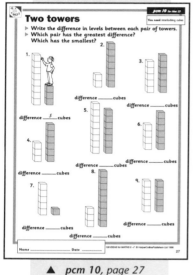
You will need
- copies of pcm 10
- interlocking cubes

Purposes
- To add two single-digit numbers (totals up to 20).
- To find the difference between two single-digit numbers.
- To recognise addition bonds to 20.
- To understand 'taller', 'shorter', 'tallest', 'shortest'.

23 i The children write the difference in the number of cubes between each pair of towers on pcm 10 and answer the questions on the pcm. ▢I ▢P

Then ask:
> In which pairs is the white tower taller? In which is the grey tower taller?
> Which is the shortest white tower/grey tower? Which is the tallest white tower/grey tower?

ii The children make each pair of towers on pcm 10 with interlocking cubes. ▢I ▢P

Ask them to:
> Write the total number of cubes used for each pair of towers.
> How many extra cubes are needed to make each white tower ten cubes high? How many to make each grey tower reach ten cubes?
> How many extra cubes are needed to make each pair total 20?

24 The children use interlocking cubes to make pairs of towers of different heights. They explore the difference between each pair, then order them from smallest to greatest difference. They repeat the ordering activity for the total of each pair. ▢P ▢G

25 i Ask the children to find pairs of towers which have the same difference in levels, e.g. 3 and 2, 7 and 8, 6 and 5 all have a difference of one. ▢P ▢G

ii Ask them to find how many different pairs of towers can be built with 13 cubes. Investigate their differences. Ask *Why are the differences always odd numbers?* They investigate using different numbers of cubes. ▢P ▢G

Answers

23 i The differences are:
1.5	2.5	3.1
4.3	5.1	6.2
7.4	8.6	9.0.

The pair in 8 has the greatest difference, the pair in 9 the smallest. The white tower is taller in 1, 5, 7. The grey tower is taller for 2, 3, 4, 6, 8. The towers are the same height in 9.

ii The totals are:
1.11	2.9	3.11
4.9	5.15	6.10
7.6	8.12	9.10.

The numbers of cubes needed to make each white tower 10 (20) cubes high are:
1.2 (12) 2.8 (18)
3.5 (15) 4.7 (17)
5.2 (12) 6.6 (16)
7.5 (15) 8.7 (17)
9.5 (15).
The numbers of cubes needed to make each grey tower 10 (20) cubes high are:
1.7 (17) 2.3 (13)
3.4 (14) 4.4 (14)
5.3 (13) 6.4 (14)
7.9 (19) 8.1 (11)
9.5 (15).

25 ii With 13 cubes the heights of the towers can be 12 and 1 (difference 11), 11 and 2 (difference 9), 10 and 3 (difference 7), 9 and 4 (difference 5), 8 and 5 (difference 3), 7 and 6 (difference 1).

Three towers

Purposes
- To add three single-digit numbers.
- To find the difference between two single-digit numbers.
- To understand 'taller', 'shorter', 'tallest', 'shortest'.
- To find sets of triples which have a given total.

You will need
- copies of pcm 11
- interlocking cubes

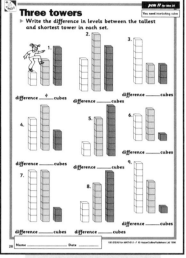

▲ **pcm 11, page 28**

26 **i** The children write the difference in the number of cubes between the tallest and shortest tower in each set on pcm 11 and answer the questions on the pcm. `I` `P`

Then ask:
- ▸ *Write the differences between the white and black towers, the white and grey towers, the black and grey towers in each set.*
- ▸ *In which sets is the white tower tallest, in which is the grey tower tallest, in which is the black tower tallest?*
- ▸ *Which is the shortest white tower? Grey tower? Black tower?*
- ▸ *Which is the tallest white tower? Grey tower? Black tower?*

ii The children make each set of towers on pcm 11 with interlocking cubes. `I` `P`

Then ask:
- ▸ *Write the total number of cubes used for each set of towers.*
- ▸ *Which set uses the most cubes? The least cubes?*

27 The children use interlocking cubes to make sets of three towers of different heights, each tower within a set a different colour. They explore the total number of cubes in each set, and the differences between pairs of towers of different colours. `P` `G`

28 Ask the children to find how many different sets of three towers can be built with 12 cubes. They investigate using different numbers of cubes. `P` `G`

Answers
26 i The differences between tallest and shortest are:
1. 4 2. 4 3. 4
4. 4 5. 6 6. 4
7. 6 8. 5 9. 7.

The differences between the white and black towers are:
1. 4 2. 2 3. 4
4. 2 5. 6 6. 3
7. 6 8. 5 9. 7.

The differences between the white and grey towers are:
1. 2 2. 4 3. 4
4. 2 5. 4 6. 1
7. 0 8. 3 9. 3.

The differences between the grey and black towers are:
1. 2 2. 2 3. 0
4. 4 5. 2 6. 4
7. 6 8. 2 9. 4.

ii The totals are:
1. 12 2. 21 (most)
3. 13 4. 15 5. 16
6. 10 (fewest)
7. 18 8. 17 9. 14.

28 With 12 cubes, the different possible sets of three are:
(1, 1, 10), (1, 2, 9),
(1, 3, 8), (1, 4, 7),
(1, 5, 6), (2, 2, 8),
(2, 3, 7), (2, 4, 6),
(2, 5, 5), (3, 3, 6),
(3, 4, 5), (4, 4, 4).

Strips

You will need
- copies of pcm 12
- interlocking cubes

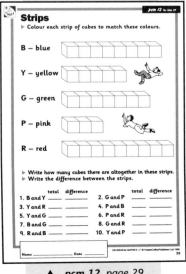

▲ **pcm 12, page 29**

Purposes
- To count a set of objects up to ten.
- To add two single-digit numbers.
- To recognise the difference between two single-digit numbers.
- To recognise addition bonds to 10 and to 20.
- To compare lengths directly, and order them.

29 **i** The children write how many cubes there are altogether in the pairs of strips and the difference between the pairs, on pcm 12. `I` `P`

ii The children make models of each strip, using interlocking cubes. `I` `P`

Then ask:
- ▸ *Put them in order according to length.*

▸ *Which strip is the longest? Which is the shortest?*
▸ *Write them in order, shortest to longest.*

Ask, *How many cubes need be added to each strip to make ten altogether? How many to make 20?*

30 The children construct their own strips of different lengths, using interlocking cubes. Each strip is a different colour. They then explore the total number of cubes in different pairs of strips, and the differences between pairs of strips. [P][G]

Answers

29 i The totals are:
1. 13   2. 10   3. 14
4. 11   5. 12   6. 12
7. 15   8. 16   9. 17
10. 8.
The differences are:
1. 3   2. 4   3. 4

4. 5   5. 2   6. 6
7. 1   8. 2   9. 1   10. 2
ii The order according to length is: pink (shortest), yellow, green, blue, red (longest).

30 The numbers are:
B: 2 (12)   C: 5 (15)
G: 3 (13)   P: 7 (17)
R: 1 (11).

Cuboids

You will need
- copies of pcm 13
- interlocking cubes

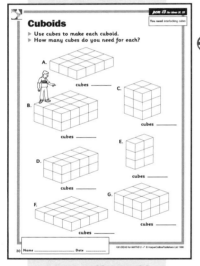

▲ *pcm 13, page 30*

Purposes
- To recognise and construct cuboids.
- To introduce the concept of volume of a cuboid.
- To interpret 2-D drawings of 3-D objects.
- To introduce the concept of area of surface.

31 **i** The children build each cuboid on pcm 13, then find how many cubes are needed to build each one. [I][P][G]

Ask them to:
▸ *Put the cuboids in order according to the number of cubes (volume), fewest first.*
▸ *Find the height of each, then the length and width.*
▸ *Put the cuboids in order according to height, smallest first.*
▸ *Find how many cubes there are in each layer of each cuboid, and how many layers each has.*
▸ *Find the volumes of the cuboids if each has an extra layer, extra two layers.*

ii The children use interlocking cubes to make their own set of cuboids and order them according to different criteria, i.e. total number of cubes (volume), height, length, width of cuboid. [I][P][G]

32 The children investigate how many different cuboids they can build, using exactly 12 cubes, 24 cubes. [P][G]

33 The children investigate the surface area of each cuboid on pcm 13 by counting squares. [P][G]

Answers

31 i The volumes are:
A. 12 B. 24 C. 12 D. 16
E. 6 F. 16 G. 18.
The heights, lengths and widths are: A: 1, 4, 3;
B: 2, 4, 3; C: 3, 2, 2;
D: 2, 4, 2; E: 3, 2, 1;
F: 1, 4, 4; G: 2, 3, 3.
The order of the cuboids according to volume (smallest first) is: E, A and C; D and F; G; B.
The order according to height (smallest first) is: A and F, B, D and G, C and E.

The number of cubes in each layer and the number of layers is:
A: 1 layer of 12 = 12;
B: 2 layers of 12 = 24;
C: 3 layers of 4 = 12;
D: 2 layers of 8 = 16;
E: 3 layers of 2 = 6;
F: 1 layer of 16 = 16;
G: 2 layers of 9 = 18.
The volume of each cuboid in cubes, if each has an extra layer (two layers) is:
A: 24 (36); B: 36 (48);
C: 16 (20); D: 24 (32);
E: 8 (10); F: 32 (48);

G: 27 (36).
32 With 12 cubes, the possibilities are: 1 x 1 x 12;
1 x 2 x 6; 1 x 3 x 4;
2 x 2 x 3.
With 24 cubes, the possibilities are: 1 x 1 x 24;
1 x 2 x 12; 1 x 3 x 8;
1 x 4 x 6; 2 x 2 x 6;
2 x 3 x 4.
33 The surface areas are:
A. 38   B. 52   C. 32
D. 40   E. 22
F. 48   G. 42.

Two towers

You need interlocking cubes

▶ Write the difference in levels between each pair of towers.
▶ Which pair has the greatest difference?
   Which has the smallest?

1.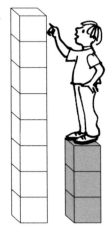

difference ___5___ cubes

2.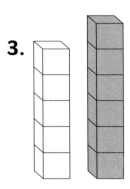

difference _____ cubes

3.

difference _____ cubes

4.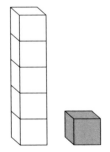

difference _____ cubes

5.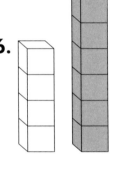

difference _____ cubes

6.

difference _____ cubes

7.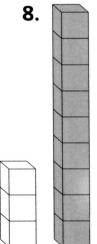

difference _____ cubes

8.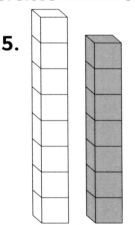

difference _____ cubes

9.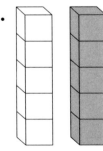

difference _____ cubes

Name .... Date ....

100 IDEAS for MATHS 5 –7 © HarperCollins*Publishers* Ltd 1996

You need interlocking cubes

Three towers

▶ Write the difference in levels between the tallest
and shortest tower in each set.

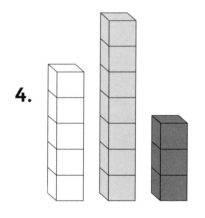

2.

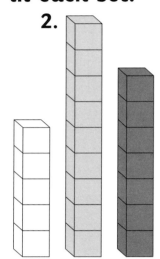

3.

difference ___4___ cubes

difference _____ cubes

difference _____ cubes

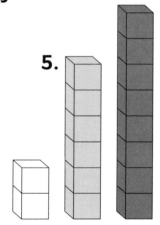

5.

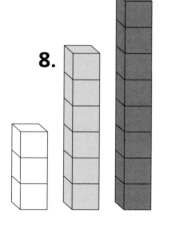

6.

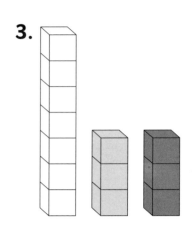

difference _____ cubes

difference _____ cubes

difference _____ cubes

9.

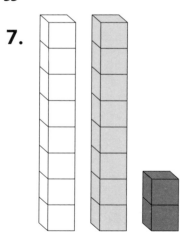

8.

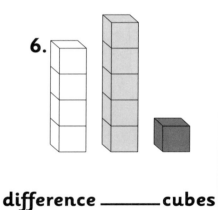

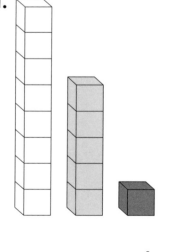

difference _____ cubes

difference _____ cubes

difference _____ cubes

Name .... Date ....

Strips

▶ **Colour each strip of cubes to match these colours.**

B – blue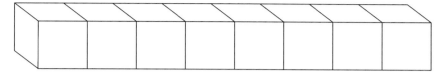

Y – yellow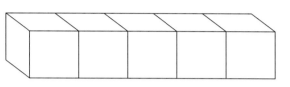

G – green

P – pink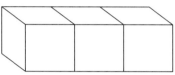

R – red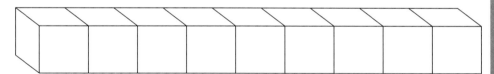

▶ **Write how many cubes there are altogether in these strips.**
▶ **Write the difference between the strips.**

	total	difference			total	difference
1. B and Y	____	_____	2. G and P		____	_____
3. Y and R	____	_____	4. P and B		____	_____
5. Y and G	____	_____	6. P and R		____	_____
7. B and G	____	_____	8. G and R		____	_____
9. R and B	____	_____	10. Y and P		____	_____

Name .... Date ....

100 IDEAS for MATHS 5–7 © HarperCollins*Publishers* Ltd 1996

Cuboids

▶ **Use cubes to make each cuboid.**
▶ **How many cubes do you need for each?**

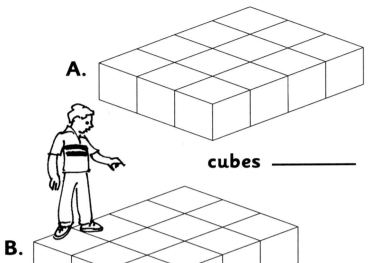

A.

cubes —————

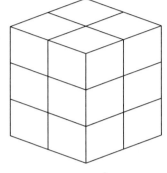

C.

cubes —————

B.

cubes —————

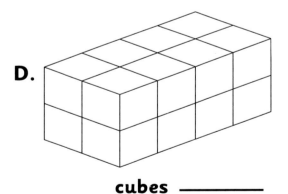

D.

cubes —————

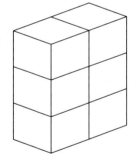

E.

cubes —————

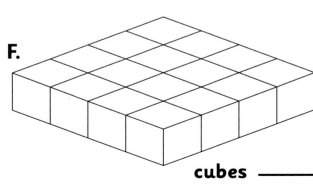

F.

cubes —————

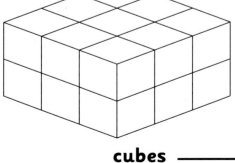

G.

cubes —————

Name .... **Date** ....

100 IDEAS for MATHS 5 –7 © HarperCollins*Publishers* Ltd 1996

Missing numbers

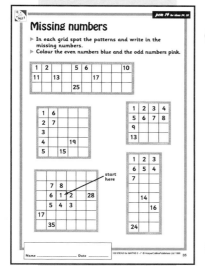

You will need
- copies of pcm 14
- square grid paper
- 1–36 number cards

▲ *pcm 14, page 35*

Purposes
- To write numbers in order in a sequence.
- To recognise odd and even numbers.
- To recognise number patterns.
- To recognise numbers in the x 2, x 3, x 5 multiplication tables.

34 **i** The children find the patterns and write in the missing numbers on the grids on pcm 14, then answer the questions on the pcm. Ask, *What patterns do the odd and even numbers make?* Discuss the fact that in some cases the odd and even numbers appear in columns, in other cases in sloping lines, creating a chequered pattern. `I P`

Note
Counters can be placed on the completed grids to highlight patterns, e.g. every even number, instead of colouring them. (The pcm can be enlarged when photocopied.)

ii Instead of highlighting odd and even numbers, the children search for other patterns and colour other sets of numbers. For example, the numbers in the x 3 or x 5 table. `I P`

35 **A game for two or three players**, using a set of 1–36 number cards and pcm 14. Use the pcm as the playing board. Each player uses a different coloured pen. Shuffle the cards and place them in a pile, face down. Take turns to turn over the top card. Write the number in its correct position on any one of the grids. The winner is the first player to make a straight line of three of their own numbers. `P G`

36 Provide the children with square grid paper and invite them to create their own grids with missing numbers. They give them to partners to solve. `P G`

Answers
34 **i** The completed grids and patterns of odd and even numbers are:

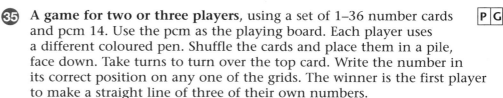

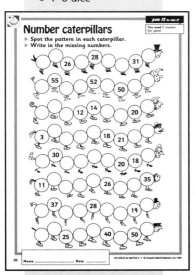

You will need
- copies of pcm 15
- squared grid paper
- counters
- 1–6 dice

▲ *pcm 15, page 36*

Number caterpillars

Purposes
- To write numbers in order in a sequence.
- To recognise number patterns.
- To create sequences.
- To recognise odd and even numbers.
- To recognise numbers in the x 2, x 3, x 5 multiplication tables.

37 **i** The children 'spot the pattern' on each caterpillar on pcm 15 and write in the missing numbers. `I P`

Then ask:
> ▸ *Describe each sequence. Is it a forwards or backwards sequence? Does the sequence jump in ones, twos, threes ...? In the completed sequence are the numbers all odd? All even? Alternating odd and even?*

Note

The children can highlight the odd and even numbers by colouring them, say, blue for odd, yellow for even.

ii A game for two players, using pcm 15 and five counters. Player A chooses one of the number sequence caterpillars and places five counters on it, to cover any five numbers, without Player B seeing which. This is then shown to Player B who has to name a hidden number before removing the counter. This is repeated five times, once for each counter. The number of correct predictions is scored out of five. The players swap roles. They play several rounds each. [P]

38 Provide the children with square grid paper and invite them to create their own number sequence strips with missing numbers. They write the answers on a separate sheet, then give the strips to partners to try out. [P] [G]

39 **A sequence game for two players**, using a dice. Players take turns to throw a dice, once for the starting number in a sequence, then again for the 'jump' number: for example, if a 2 is thrown, followed by a 5, then the sequence begins; 2, 7, 12, 17 ... Players write the first eight numbers in their sequence. They check each other's sequences. They play several rounds each. [P]

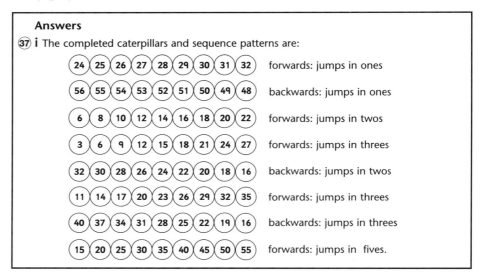

Answers

37 i The completed caterpillars and sequence patterns are:

24 25 26 27 28 29 30 31 32   forwards: jumps in ones

56 55 54 53 52 51 50 49 48   backwards: jumps in ones

6 8 10 12 14 16 18 20 22   forwards: jumps in twos

3 6 9 12 15 18 21 24 27   forwards: jumps in threes

32 30 28 26 24 22 20 18 16   backwards: jumps in twos

11 14 17 20 23 26 29 32 35   forwards: jumps in threes

40 37 34 31 28 25 22 19 16   backwards: jumps in threes

15 20 25 30 35 40 45 50 55   forwards: jumps in fives.

You will need
- copies of pcm 16
- counters
- 1–6 dice
- cubes

▲ *pcm 16, page 37*

Counter patterns

Purposes
- To recognise number patterns.
- To recognise and create sequences of numbers.
- To recognise numbers in the x2, x3, x4, x5, multiplication tables.

40 The children put counters on the multiples of three: 3, 6, 9 ... on pcm 16 and investigate the patterns the counters make. They remove the counters and do the same for the multiples of five. [I] [P]

Note

Instead of placing counters on the numbers, the children can colour the squares.

Then ask:
> ▸ *Investigate patterns in the counters placed on other multiples, e.g. twos, fours, etc.*

(Discuss the fact that some of the patterns have counters in columns, some have them in sloping lines.)

41 More activities for pcm 16: [P] [G]
  ▸ *Investigate how many numbers there are on the grid in the x 2 sequence. Extend this to the x 3, x 4, x 5 ...sequences. Create a table to show the results.*
  ▸ *Investigate which numbers appear in two different sequences, e.g. 6 and 12 appear in both the x 2 and x 3 sequences.*
  ▸ *List the first ten numbers in different multiples.*

42 **A game of 'Threes' for two players**, using pcm 16, counters and a dice. [P]
The players each place a counter at Start. They take turns to throw the dice, and move their counter a matching number of spaces along the numbers on the grid. If they land on a multiple of three, they collect a cube. When both players reach Finish, the winner is the one who has collected most cubes. They play again, but start at Finish and move backwards to Start.

Variation
Change the winning numbers from multiples of three to multiples of two or five, for example.

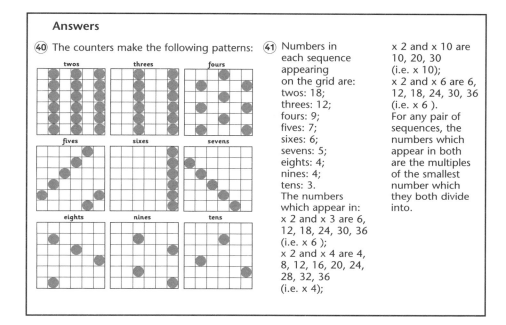

Answers

40 The counters make the following patterns:

41 Numbers in each sequence appearing on the grid are:
twos: 18;
threes: 12;
fours: 9;
fives: 7;
sixes: 6;
sevens: 5;
eights: 4;
nines: 4;
tens: 3.
The numbers which appear in:
x 2 and x 3 are 6, 12, 18, 24, 30, 36 (i.e. x 6);
x 2 and x 4 are 4, 8, 12, 16, 20, 24, 28, 32, 36 (i.e. x 4);
x 2 and x 10 are 10, 20, 30 (i.e. x 10);
x 2 and x 6 are 6, 12, 18, 24, 30, 36 (i.e. x 6).
For any pair of sequences, the numbers which appear in both are the multiples of the smallest number which they both divide into.

You will need
● copies of pcm 17 and 18
● counters (two colours)
● dice
● number cards

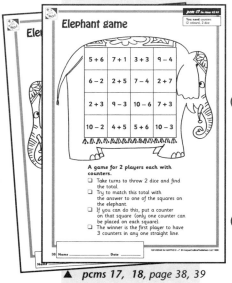

▲ *pcms 17, 18, page 38, 39*

Elephant games

Purposes
● To recognise addition and subtraction facts up to 12.
● To create additions and subtractions with a given answer.
● To investigate all possible outcomes when throwing two dice.
● To work systematically.

43 **Elephant game** A game for two players, each with a set of counters of their own colour, using pcm 17 and two dice. Players try to match the totals on the board with their dice throws and aim to have three counters in a straight line. (*See* pcm 17 for rules.) [P]

Variation
Players continue until all the squares contain a counter. (*See* pcm 17 for rules.)

44 More activities for pcm 17: [P]
  ▸ *Investigate all the answers to the additions and subtractions in the 16 parts of the elephant:*
  ▸ *Which answers occur more than once?*

▸ *Find which answers result from adding, which from taking away.*
▸ *Invent a different addition or subtraction with the same answer
  as those in each part of the elephant.*

45 The children invent their own Elephant Game, based on the totals `P G`
made when throwing two dice. First they find what the possible totals
are, then randomly spread these out on the elephant grid on pcm 18,
including some more than once. Finally they create additions and
subtractions whose answers match these numbers, and play the game.

46 Again using pcm 18, the children invent a similar Elephant Game `P G`
based not on the total when throwing two dice, but on one of these:

(a) the score when throwing one dice;
(b) the number when turning over the top card of a pack
    of numbered cards;
(c) the difference between the two scores when two dice
    are rolled.

Answers

44 The answers to the squares on the elephant are:

11	8	6	5
4	7	3	9
5	6	4	10
8	9	11	7

The answers 3 and 10 appear once only.
The answers 4, 5, 6, 7, 8, 9 and 11 appear twice.
The answers 5, 6, 7, 8, 9 (twice), 10, 11 (twice) result from additions.
The answers 3, 4 (twice), 5, 6, 7, 8 result from subtractions.

Missing numbers

▶ In each grid spot the patterns and write in the missing numbers.

▶ Colour the even numbers blue and the odd numbers pink.

1	2			5	6				10
11		13				17			
			25						

1	6		
2	7		
3			
4		19	
5		15	

1	2	3	4
5	6	7	8
9			
13			

start here

	7	8		
	6	1	2	28
	5	4	3	
17				
35				

1	2	3
6	5	4
7		
	14	
		16
24		

You need 5 counters
(for game)

Number caterpillars

▶ Spot the pattern in each caterpillar.
▶ Write in the missing numbers.

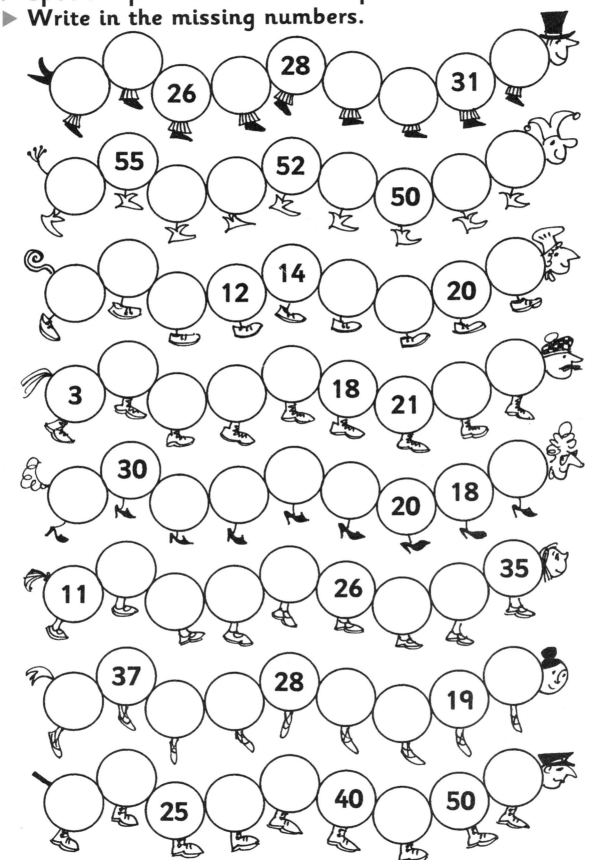

Name .... Date ....

100 IDEAS for MATHS 5 –7 © HarperCollinsPublishers Ltd 1996

Counter patterns

You need counters

▶ Put counters on the numbers in the 3 times table:
3, 6, 9 ... Look for patterns.

▶ Remove the counters, then put them on the
numbers in the 5 times table: 5, 10, 15 ...

start

1	2	3	4	5	6
7	8	9	10	11	12
13	14	15	16	17	18
19	20	21	22	23	24
25	26	27	28	29	30
31	32	33	34	35	36

finish

Name .... Date ....

Elephant game

You need counters
(2 colours), 2 dice

5 + 6	7 + 1	3 + 3	9 – 4
6 – 2	2 + 5	7 – 4	2 + 7
2 + 3	9 – 3	10 – 6	7 + 3
10 – 2	4 + 5	5 + 6	10 – 3

A game for 2 players each with counters.

❑ Take turns to throw 2 dice and find the total.

❑ Try to match this total with the answer to one of the squares on the elephant.

❑ If you can do this, put a counter on that square (only one counter can be placed on each square).

❑ The winner is the first player to have 3 counters in any one straight line.

100 IDEAS for MATHS 5 –7 © HarperCollins*Publishers* Ltd 1996

Name .... **Date** ....

Elephant grid

Name .... Date ....

Clock times

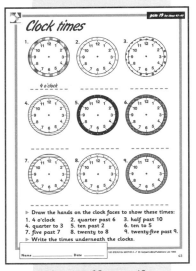

▲ *pcm 19, page 43*

Purposes
- To tell the time on an analogue clock at five minute intervals.
- To recognise minutes past and minutes to the hour in five minute intervals.
- To state the time five minutes, a quarter of an hour and half an hour after a given time.
- To state the time five minutes, a quarter of an hour and half an hour before a given time.

47 The children draw the hands on the clock faces on pcm 19 to show the times listed, then write the times under the clocks.   [I][P]

Then ask:
- ▶ *How many minutes on each clock after the last hour?*
- ▶ *How many minutes on each clock before the next hour?*
- ▶ *How many complete hours on each clock before 6 o'clock, 12 o'clock?*

(The clock face can be used to find and demonstrate the answers.)

48 Further questions for pcm 19:   [I][P]
- ▶ *Which clock shows the nearest time to now?*
- ▶ *Which shows the nearest time to 12 o'clock, 6 o'clock, 3 o'clock, 9 o'clock?*
- ▶ *What time will each clock show in ten minutes time, a quarter of an hour's time, half an hour's time?*
- ▶ *What time did each clock show ten minutes ago, a quarter of an hour ago, and half an hour ago?*

(The clock face can be used to find and demonstrate the answers.)

49 The children create their own times by drawing hands on the clock faces on pcm 19, then writing the times underneath.   [I][P]

Answers

47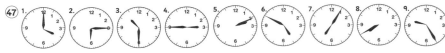

The number of minutes after the last hour:
1. 0   2. 15   3. 30   4. 45
5. 10   6. 50   7. 5   8. 40
9. 25.
The number of minutes before the next hour:
1. 60   2. 45   3. 30   4. 15
5. 50   6. 10   7. 55   8. 20
9. 35.
The number of complete hours before 6 o'clock:
1. 2   2. 11   3. 7   4. 3
5. 3   6. 1   7. 10   8. 10
9. 8.
The number of complete hours before 12 o'clock:
1. 8   2. 5   3. 1   4. 9   5. 9
6. 7   7. 4   8. 4   9. 2.

48 The nearest to 12 o'clock: 3.
The nearest to 6 o'clock: 2.
The nearest to 3 o'clock: 4.
The nearest to 8 o'clock: 8.
The time on each clock in ten minutes time:
1. ten past 4
2. twenty-five past 6
3. twenty to 11
4. five to 3
5. twenty past 2

6. 5 o'clock
7. quarter past 7
8. ten to 8
9. twenty-five to 10.

The time on each clock in 15 minutes time:
1. quarter past 4
2. half past 6
3. quarter to 11
4. 3 o'clock
5. twenty-five past 2
6. five past 5
7. twenty past 7
8. five to 8
9. twenty to 10.

The time on each clock in 30 minutes time:
1. half past 4
2. quarter to 7
3. 11 o'clock
4. quarter past 3
5. twenty to 3
6. twenty past 5
7. twenty-five to 8
8. ten past 9
9. five to 10.

The time on each clock ten minutes ago:
1. ten to 4

2. five past 6
3. twenty past 10
4. twenty-five to 3
5. 2 o'clock
6. twenty to 5
7. five to 7
8. half past 7
9. quarter past 9.

The time on each clock 15 minutes ago:
1. quarter to 4
2. 6 o'clock
3. quarter past 10
4. half past 2
5. five to 2
6. twenty-five to 5
7. ten to 7
8. twenty-five past 7
9. ten past 9.

The time on each clock 30 minutes ago:
1. half past 3
2. quarter to 6
3. 10 o'clock
4. quarter past 2
5. twenty to 2
6. twenty past 4
7. twenty-five to 7
8. ten past 7
9. five to 9.

Digital clock times

You will need
- copies of pcm 20
- demonstration digital clock face

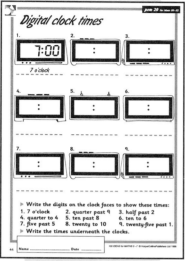

▲ *pcm 20, page 44*

Purposes
- To tell the time on a digital clock at five minute intervals.
- To recognise minutes past and minutes to the hour in five minute intervals.
- To state the time five minutes, a quarter of an hour and a half hour after a given time.
- To state the time five minutes, a quarter of an hour and a half hour before a given time.

50 The children write the digits on the clock faces on pcm 20 to show the times listed, then write the times under the clocks. `I  P`

Then ask:
- ▸ *How many minutes on each clock after the last hour?*
- ▸ *How many minutes on each clock before the next hour?*
- ▸ *How many complete hours on each clock before 12 o'clock, 3 o'clock?*

(The clock face can be used to find and demonstrate the answers.)

51 Further questions for pcm 20: `I  P`
- ▸ *Which clock shows the nearest time to now?*
- ▸ *Which shows the nearest time to 12 o'clock, 6 o'clock, 3 o'clock, 9 o'clock?*
- ▸ *What time will each clock show in five minutes time, a quarter of an hour's time, half an hour's time?*
- ▸ *What time did each clock show ten minutes ago, a quarter of an hour ago, half an hour ago?*

(The clock face can be used to find and demonstrate the answers.)

52 The children create their own times by writing digits on the clock faces on pcm 20, then writing the times underneath. `I  P`

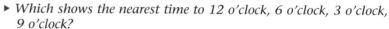

Answers

50 The digital times are:
1. 7:00   2. 9:15
3. 2:30   4. 3:45
5. 8:10   6. 5:50
7. 5:05   8. 9:40
9. 1:25.

The number of minutes after the last hour:
1. 0   2. 15   3. 30
4. 45   5. 10   6. 50
7. 5   8. 40   9. 25.

The number of minutes before the next hour:
1. 60   2. 45   3. 30   4. 15
5. 50   6. 10   7. 55   8. 20
9. 35.

The number of complete hours before 12 o'clock:
1. 5   2. 2   3. 9   4. 8
5. 3   6. 6   7. 6   8. 2
9. 10.

The number of complete hours before 3 o'clock:
1. 8   2. 5   3. 0   4. 11   5. 6
6. 9   7. 9   8. 5   9. 1.

51 The nearest to 12 o'clock: 9.
The nearest to 6 o'clock: 6.
The nearest to 3 o'clock: 3.
The nearest to 8 o'clock: 5.

The time on each clock in five minutes time:
1. 7:05   2. 9:20
3. 2:35   4. 3:50
5. 8:15   6. 5:55
7. 5:10   8. 9:45
9. 1:30.

The time on each clock in 15 minutes time:
1. 7:15   2. 9:30
3. 2:45   4. 4:00
5. 8:25   6. 6:05
7. 5:20   8. 9:55
9. 1:40.

The time on each clock in 30 minutes time:
1. 7:30   2. 9:45
3. 3:00   4. 4:15
5. 8:40   6. 6:20
7. 5:35   8. 10:10
9. 1:55.

The time on each clock ten minutes ago:
1. 6:50   2. 9:05
3. 2:20   4. 3:35
5. 8:00   6. 5:40
7. 4:55   8. 9:30
9. 1:15.

The time on each clock 15 minutes ago:
1. 6:45   2. 9:00
3. 2:15   4. 3:30
5. 7:55   6. 5:35
7. 4:50   8. 9:25
9. 1:10.

The time on each clock 30 minutes ago:
1. 6:30   2. 8:45
3. 2:00   4. 3:15
5. 7:40   6. 5:20
7. 4:35   8. 9:10
9. 12:55.

Clock game

Purposes
- To recognise the time on an analogue clock at five minute intervals.
- To recognise minutes past and minutes to the hour in five minute intervals.
- To recognise clockwise and anticlockwise turns.

Clock game

53 A game for two or more players, using pcm 21, counters and dice. [P][G]
The children throw the dice and move the counters in five-minute intervals to match the dice throw. (*See* pcm 21 for rules.)

Variation 1: Players place one counter on each point round [P][G]
the clock. If, on their turn, they move onto a space which contains a counter they keep it. When all the counters have been removed, the winner is the player who has collected the most counters.

Variation 2: Players make a set of cards, some with C for clockwise, [P][G]
and some with AC for anticlockwise, on them. The cards are shuffled and placed face down in a pile. They play the same game, but before throwing the dice also reveal the top card to decide whether to turn clockwise or anticlockwise round the clock, matching the dice throw.

▲ *pcm 21, page 45*

Calendars

Purposes
- To read and interpret a calendar.
- To recognise the relationship between days, weeks and months.
- To recognise number patterns.

54 **Ideas** Ask the children to look at the calendar for March 1996 [I][P]
on pcm 22. Discuss different aspects of time with them, e.g.:

- ▶ *What do the initials M, Tu, W ... stand for?*
- ▶ *How many days in a week? What are the names of the days?*
- ▶ *Which day comes after Wednesday, Friday ...?*
- ▶ *Which day comes before Sunday, Tuesday ...?*
- ▶ *On what day was the first day of March? What day was the second ...?*
- ▶ *What was the last date in March? On what day was the last day of March?*
- ▶ *How many days were there in the month of March?*
- ▶ *What were the dates of the Saturdays, the Wednesdays ...?*
- ▶ *How many full weeks were there in March 1996?*
- ▶ *How many days are there in other months? Which months have the same number of days?*
- ▶ *How many different months are there in a year? Say them in order.*
- ▶ *Which month comes before April, September ...? Which month comes after August, May ...?*
- ▶ *How many Mondays were there in March 1996? How many Tuesdays ...?*

55 The children write the present month's calendar on pcm 22 [I][P]
and answer the questions on the pcm.

56 The children investigate patterns in the numbers in a calendar month. [I][P]
For example: As you move along a row, the numbers jump in ones.
As you move down a column the numbers jump in sevens.
As you move diagonally from top left to bottom right, the numbers jump in eights.
As you move diagonally from top right to bottom left, the numbers jump in sixes.

▲ *pcm 22, page 46*

Answers
55 Answers depend on the month selected.

You will need
- copies of pcm 21
- long and short pointers for the clock hands
- 1–6 dice

You will need
- copies of pcm 22
- monthly calendar

Clock times

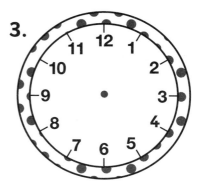
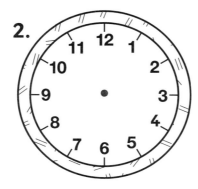

1. 2. 3.

4 o'clock

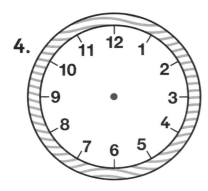

4. 5. 6.

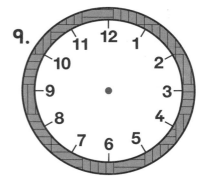
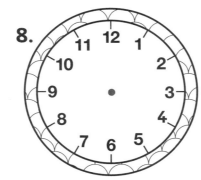

7. 8. 9.

▶ **Draw the hands on the clock faces to show these times:**

1. 4 o'clock   2. quarter past 6   3. half past 10
4. quarter to 3   5. ten past 2   6. ten to 5
7. five past 7   8. twenty to 8   9. twenty-five past 9.

▶ **Write the times underneath the clocks.**

Name .... Date ....

100 IDEAS for MATHS 5 –7 © HarperCollins*Publishers* Ltd 1996

Digital clock times

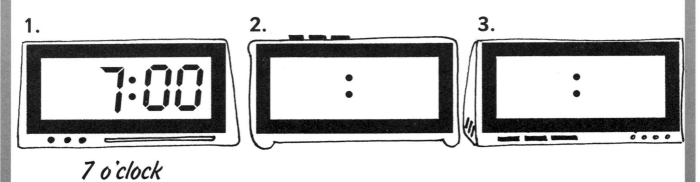

1.

7 o'clock

2.

3.

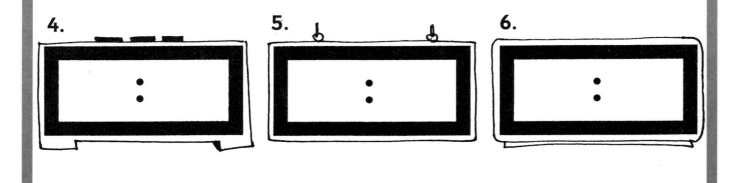

4.

5.

6.

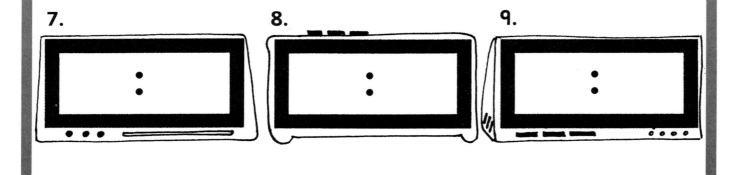

7.

8.

9.

▶ **Write the digits on the clock faces to show these times:**

1. 7 o'clock   2. quarter past 9   3. half past 2

4. quarter to 4   5. ten past 8   6. ten to 6

7. five past 5   8. twenty to 10   9. twenty-five past 1.

▶ **Write the times underneath the clocks.**

Name .... Date ....

100 IDEAS for MATHS 5–7 © HarperCollinsPublishers Ltd 1996

Clock game

You need long and short pointers for hands, a dice, counters

A clock face showing numbers 1 through 12 with counters placed around the outer edge, clock hands, and dice.

A game for two or more players.

❑ Place the pointers as hands to show 3 o'clock and put a counter at 12.

❑ Take turns to throw the dice and move the counter clockwise in five minute intervals to match the dice throw.

❑ Move the pointers and say the time, e.g. if you throw a 2 you say 'ten past 3'.

❑ Collect 1 counter if you land on 'quarter past' and say it correctly.
   2 counters if you land on 'half past' and say it correctly.
   3 counters if you land on 'quarter to' and say it correctly.
   4 counters if you land on 'o'clock' and say it correctly.

❑ The winner is the first to collect 15 counters.

Name .... Date ....

Calendars

This is the calendar for March 1996.

March 1996						
M	**Tu**	**W**	**Th**	**F**	**Sa**	**Su**
				1	2	3
4	5	6	7	8	9	10
11	12	13	14	15	16	17
18	19	20	21	22	23	24
25	26	27	28	29	30	31

▶ **Write this month's calendar.**

M	**Tu**	**W**	**Th**	**F**	**Sa**	**Su**

▶ **How many Mondays in both months?**

▶ **How many Tuesdays, Wednesdays ... Sundays in both months?**

▶ **Compare these months with other months.**

Name .... Date ....

100 IDEAS for MATHS 5 –7 © HarperCollins*Publishers* Ltd 1996

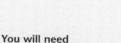

Trains and trucks

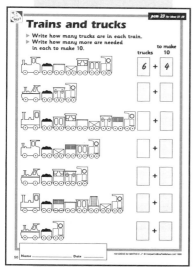

▲ *pcm 23, page 50*

Purposes
- To count a set of objects (total up to ten).
- To learn addition bonds to 10 and 20, and other numbers in between.
- To introduce the x 2 and x 4 multiplication tables.

57 The children count and write how many trucks there are on each train on pcm 23, then write how many more are needed on each to make ten. (The results can be recorded using '+' notation, e.g. 6 + 4 = 10.)   I P

Then ask:
> ▶ *Which train has most trucks? Which has fewest?*
> ▶ *How many trucks are needed to make other numbers, e.g. 12, 20?*
> ▶ *Colour each truck either red or blue. Count how many there are of each colour.*
> ▶ *Write an addition bond for the numbers of each colour on each train.*

58 Further activities for pcm 22:   P G
> ▶ *Each truck has two wheels. Find the number of wheels on different numbers of trucks.*
> ▶ *Write the number of wheels on the trucks of each train.*
> ▶ *Write the number of wheels on trains which have 1 truck, 2 trucks … 10 trucks, (leading to the x 2 table).*
> ▶ *Repeat these activities for trucks with four wheels (leading to the x 4 table).*

Answers

57 The number of trucks and the number needed to make ten:
1. 6,4   2. 3,7   3. 8,2
4. 5,5   5. 4,6   6. 7,3
7. 2,8.
3. has most trucks, 7. has fewest.

The number of trucks needed to make 12 (20):
1. 6(14)   2. 9(17)

58 3. 4(12)   4. 7(15)
5. 8(16)   6. 5(13)
7. 10(18).

The number of wheels, assuming each truck has two wheels:
1.12   2.6   3.16
4.10   5.8   6.14
7.4.

The number of wheels on trains which have one truck … 10 trucks (x 2 table):
2, 4, 6, 8, 10, 12, 14, 16, 18, 20.

The number of wheels, assuming each truck has four wheels:
1.24   2.12   3.32
4.20   5.16   6.28
7.8.

Buttons

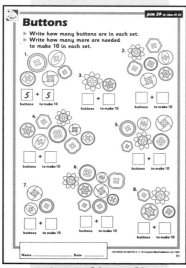

▲ *pcm 24, page 51*

Purposes
- To count a set of objects (total up to ten).
- To learn addition bonds to 10 and 20, and other numbers in between.
- To introduce the x 4 multiplication table.

59 The children count and write how many buttons there are in each set on pcm 24, then write how many more are needed in each set to make ten. (The results can be recorded using '+' notation, e.g. 8 + 2 = 10.)   I P

Then ask:
> ▶ *Which set has most buttons? Which has fewest?*
> ▶ *How many buttons are needed to make other numbers, e.g. 12, 20?*
> ▶ *Colour each button either yellow or blue. Count how many there are of each colour.*
> ▶ *Write an addition bond for the numbers of each colour in each set.*

60 Further activities for pcm 24:   I P G
> ▶ *Each button has four holes. Investigate the number of holes in different sets of buttons.*

> ▸ *Write the total number of holes in the buttons of each set.*
> ▸ *Write the total number of holes in one button, two buttons*
>   *... ten buttons (leading to the x 4 table).*

(61) **A game for 2 players**, using ten buttons. Player A takes some of the buttons, unseen by Player B, who then counts how many are left, and says how many have been taken. They check to see if he/she is correct, then swap roles. Extend the activity by changing the number of buttons. `P`

Answers

(59) The number of buttons in each set and the number needed to make ten:
1. 5,5   2. 2,8   3. 7,3
4. 8,2   5. 6,4   6. 3,7
7. 9,1   8. 4,6.
7. has most buttons,
2. has least.

The number of buttons needed to make 12(20):
1. 7(15)   2. 10(18)
3. 5(13)   4. 4(12)
5. 6(14)   6. 9(17)
7. 3(11)   8. 8(16).

(60) The number of holes in each set are:
1. 20   2. 8   3. 28
4. 32   5. 24   6. 12
7. 36   8. 16.

The number of holes in 1 button ... 10 buttons (x4 table):
4, 8, 12, 16, 20, 24, 28, 32, 36, 40.

Number mobiles

Purposes
- To recognise addition bonds to ten, and to other numbers greater than ten.
- To find differences between two numbers.
- To work systematically.

(62) The children complete the mobiles on pcm 25 so that the total of the two numbers on the left balances the number on the right. They balance ten, then twelve, then invent their own number mobiles. `I` `P`

Then ask:
> ▸ *How many different ways are there of balancing ten and twelve?*
> ▸ *How many different ways are there of balancing other numbers?*

(63) The children use a set of 1–9 number cards. They draw a large outline of a mobile like those on pcm 25 (or enlarge one on pcm 25). They place three cards in position on the mobile so that the total of the two numbers on the left balances the number on the right, then investigate how many different ways of balancing they can find. `I` `P`

(64) Change the rules for balancing the mobiles on pcm 25: for example, the *difference* between the two numbers on the left must balance the number on the right. Ask the children to write different mobiles to balance ten on the right, then twelve on the right. Restrict the numbers initially to, say, 20 or less. The children repeat idea 63, using the 1–7 number cards but the difference between the two numbers on the left must balance the number on the right. `I` `P`

You will need
- copies of pcm 25
- 1–9 number cards

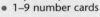

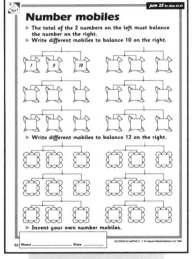

▲ *pcm 25, page 52*

Answers

(62) Ways of balancing ten on the right include these pairs on the left:
(1 and 9), (2 and 8), (3 and 7), (4 and 6), (5 and 5).
Ways of balancing 12 on the right include these pairs on the left:
(1 and 11), (2 and 10), (3 and 9), (4 and 8), (5 and 7), (6 and 6).

(63) There are 16 ways of balancing 1–9 number cards:
(1 and 2; 3), (1 and 3; 4), (1 and 4; 5), (2 and 3; 5),

(1 and 5; 6), (2 and 4; 6), (1 and 6; 7),
(2 and 5; 7), (3 and 4; 7), (1 and 7; 8), (2 and 6; 8), (3 and 5; 8), (1 and 8; 9), (2 and 7; 9), (3 and 6; 9), (4 and 5; 9).

(64) **i** Ways of balancing ten on the right include these pairs on the left:
(1 and 11), (2 and 12), (3 and 13), (4 and 14), (5 and 15), (6 and 16), and so on.
Ways of balancing 12 on the right include

these pairs on the left:
(1 and 13), (2 and 14), (3 and 15), (4 and 16), (5 and 17), (6 and 18), and so on.

ii There are 15 ways of balancing the 1–7 number cards;
(2 and 3; 1), (3 and 4; 1), (4 and 5; 1), (5 and 6; 1), (1 and 3; 2), (3 and 5; 2), (4 and 6; 2), (1 and 4; 3), (2 and 5; 3), (4 and 7; 3), (1 and 5; 4), (2 and 6; 4), (1 and 6; 5), (2 and 7; 5), (1 and 7; 6).

More number mobiles

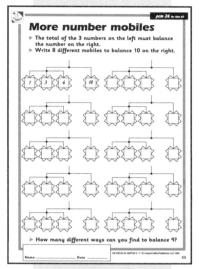

▲ *pcm 26, page 53*

Purposes
- To add three single-digit numbers.
- To recognise sets of three numbers which have a given total.
- To split four numbers into pairs with equal totals.
- To work systematically.

65 The children complete the mobiles on pcm 26 so that the total `I` `P`
of the three numbers on the left balances the number on the right.
They make eight different mobiles to balance ten, then investigate
how many different mobiles they can find to balance nine.

Then ask:
- *How many different ways are there of balancing 8 and 12?*
- *How many different ways are there of balancing other numbers?*

66 The children use a set of 1–9 number cards. They draw a large `I` `P`
outline of a mobile like those on pcm 26 (or enlarge one on pcm 26).
They place four cards in position on the mobile so that the total
of the three numbers on the left balances the number on the right,
then investigate how many different ways of balancing they can find.

67 The children use a set of 1–9 number cards. Provide large outline `I` `P` `G`
mobiles like this (or ask the children to draw them). Ask the
children to investigate ways of balancing the numbers on the mobile.

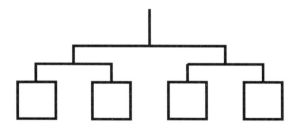

Answers

65 The eight ways
of balancing ten
on the right are these
eight sets on the left:
(1,1,8), (1 2,7), (1,3,6),
(1,4,5), (2,2,6), (2,3,5),
(2,4,4), (3,3,4).
The seven ways
of balancing nine
on the right have these
eight sets on the left:
(1,1,7), (1,2,6), (1,3,5),
(1,4,4), (2,2,5), (2,3,4),
(3,3,3).
There are five ways
of balancing eight:
(1,1,6), (1,2,5), (1,3,4),
(2,2,4), (2,3,3).
There are 12 ways
of balancing 12:
(1,2,9), (1,3,8), (1,4,7),
(1 5,6), (2,2,8), (2,3,7),
(2,4,6), (2,5,5), (3,3,6),
(3,4,5), (4,4,4).

66 There are only six different
ways:
(1,2 and 6;9),
(1,3 and 5;9),
(1,2 and 5;8),
(1,3 and 4;8),
(1,2 and 4;7),
(1,2 and 3;6).

67 There are 34
different possibilities:
5 on each side:
(1,4 and 2,3)
6 on each side:
(1,5 and 2,4)
7 on each side:
(1,6 and 2,5),
(1,6 and 3,4),
(2,5 and 3,4)
8 on each side:
(1,7 and 2,6),
(1,7 and 3,5),
(2,6 and 3,5)
9 on each side:
(1,8 and 2,7),
(1,8 and 3,6),
(1,8 and 4,5),
(2,7 and 3,6),
(2,7 and 4,5),

(3,6 and 4,5)
10 on each side:
(1,9 and 2,8),
(1,9 and 3,7),
(1, 9 and 4,6),
(2,8 and 3,7),
(2,8 and 4,6),
(3,7 and 4,6).
11 on each side:
(2,9 and 3,8),
(2,9 and 4,7),
(2,9 and 5,6),
(3,8 and 4,7),
(3,8 and 5,6),
(4,7 and 5,6)
12 on each side:
(3,9 and 4,8),
(3,9 and 5,7),
(4,8 and 5,7)
13 on each side:
(4,9 and 5,8),
(4,9 and 6,7),
(5,8 and 6,7)
14 on each side:
(5,9 and 6,8)
15 on each side:
(6,9 and 7,8).

Trains and trucks

▶ Write how many trucks are in each train.
▶ Write how many more are needed
  in each to make 10.

trucks   to make
10

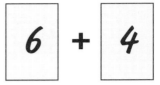
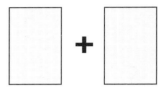

trucks		to make 10
6	+	*4*
	+	

| | + | |

| | + | |

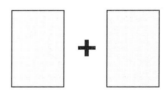

| | + | |

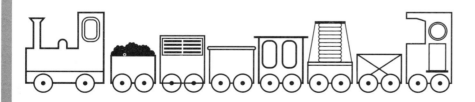
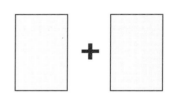

| | + | |

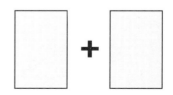

| | + | |

| | + | |

Name .... Date ....

100 IDEAS for MATHS 5 –7 © HarperCollins*Publishers* Ltd 1996

Buttons

▶ Write how many buttons are in each set.
▶ Write how many more are needed
to make 10 in each set.

1.

5	+	5

buttons   to make 10

2.

	+	

buttons   to make 10

3.

	+	

buttons   to make 10

4.

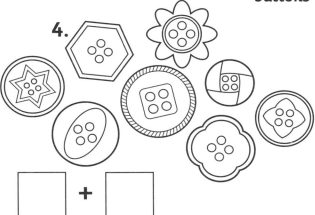

	+	

buttons   to make 10

5.

	+	

buttons   to make 10

6.

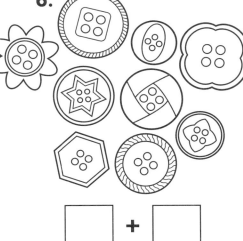

	+	

buttons   to make 10

7.

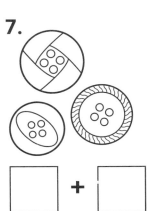

	+	

buttons   to make 10

8.

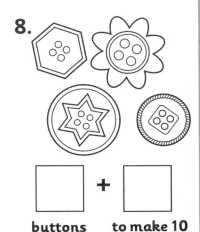

	+	

buttons   to make 10

Name .... Date ....

100 IDEAS for MATHS 5–7 © HarperCollins*Publishers* Ltd 1996

Number mobiles

▶ **The total of the 2 numbers on the left must balance the number on the right.**

▶ **Write different mobiles to balance 10 on the right.**

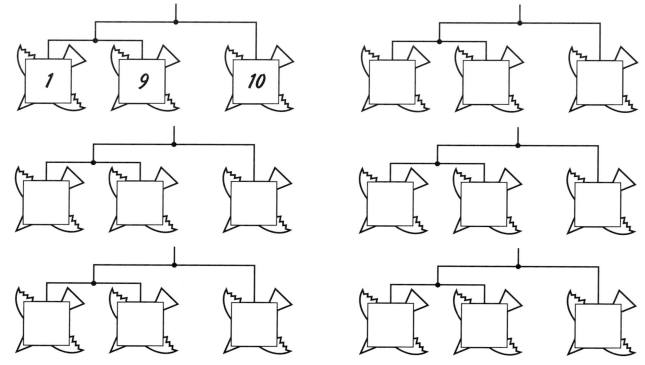

▶ **Write different mobiles to balance 12 on the right.**

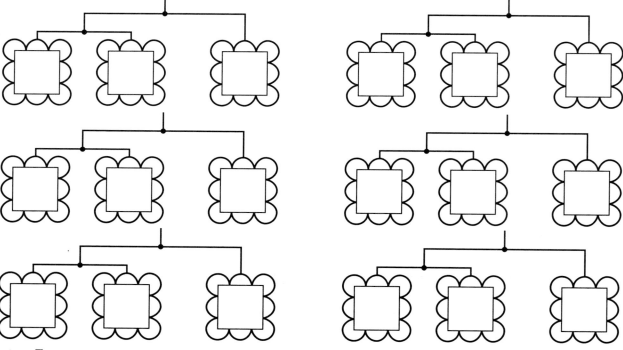

▶ **Invent your own number mobiles.**

Name .... Date ....

More number mobiles

▶ The total of the 3 numbers on the left must balance the number on the right.

▶ Write 8 different mobiles to balance 10 on the right.

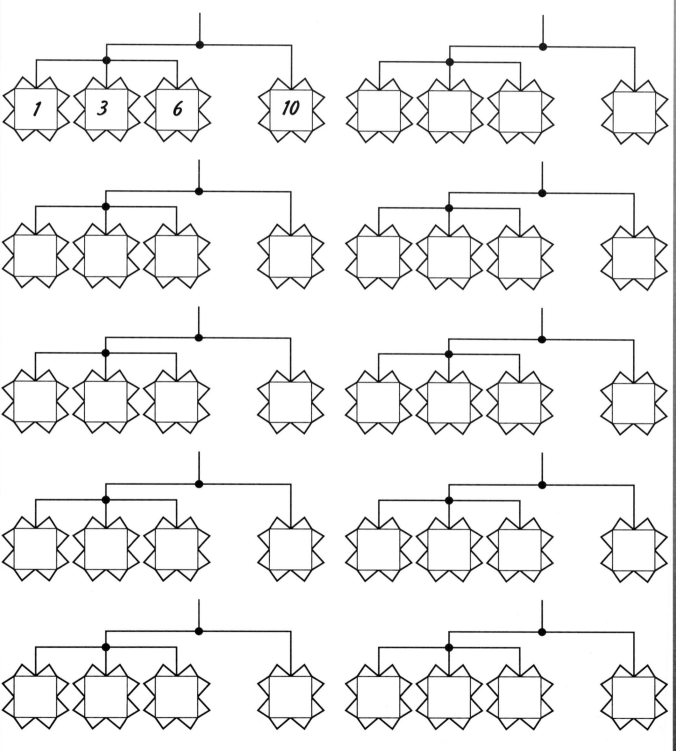

▶ **How many different ways can you find to balance 9?**

100 IDEAS for MATHS 5 –7 © HarperCollins*Publishers* Ltd 1996

Name .... Date ....

You will need
- copies of pcm 27
- 6 dice
- counters (two colours)

▲ pcm 27, *page 57*

 # Football games

Purposes
- To add two single-digit numbers.
- To add three or more single-digit numbers.
- To recognise the difference between two single-digit numbers.

68 *Game 1* A game for two players, each with counters of their own colour, using pcm 27 and two dice. The aim is to match the dice totals with a shirt number, to 'score a goal' (*see* pcm 27 for rules). ⬜P

Variation 1
Players place a counter on a shirt which matches either the total or the difference between the two dice numbers. ⬜P

Variation 2
The children play their own football game based on the total of three dice, first deciding what numbers to put on the shirts. ⬜P

Variation 3
The children play a game with shirts numbered from 5–20 and choose the number of dice. (Blank out the numbers on pcm 27 and recopy.)

69 The children find how many shirts there are with each number. They throw two dice and investigate the different possible totals, then the possible differences for covering each shirt number. ⬜P⬜G

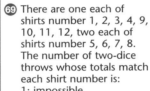

Answers

69 There are one each of shirts number 1, 2, 3, 4, 9, 10, 11, 12, two each of shirts number 5, 6, 7, 8. The number of two-dice throws whose totals match each shirt number is:
1: impossible
2: (1 and 1)
3: (1 and 2)
4: (1 and 3), (2 and 2)
5: (1 and 4), (2 and 3)

6: (1 and 5), (2 and 4), (3 and 3)
7: (1 and 6), (2 and 5), (3 and 4)
8: (2 and 6), (3 and 5), (4 and 4)
9: (3 and 6), (4 and 5)
10: (5 and 5), (4 and 6)
11: (5 and 6)
12: (6 and 6).

The number of two-dice throws whose differences match each shirt number is:
1: (1 and 2), (2 and 3), (3 and 4), (4 and 5), (5 and 6)
2: (1 and 3), (2 and 4), (3 and 5), (4 and 6)
3: (1 and 4), (2 and 5), (3 and 6)
4: (1 and 5), (2 and 6)
5: (1 and 6).

You will need
- copies of pcm 28
- cm rulers
- 1–8 number cards
- counters (two colours)

▲ pcm 28, *page 58*

 # Fishing games

Purposes
- To compare lengths measured in centimetres.
- To measure lengths in centimetres.
- To estimate lengths in centimetres.
- To recognise the difference between two lengths in centimetres.

70 *Game 1* A game for two players, each with counters of their own colour, using pcm 28, 1–8 number cards and a centimetre ruler. The aim is to get a counter on the fisher with the longest fishing rod (*see* pcm 28 for rules). ⬜P

Variation 1
The children play as above but measure the length of their fishing rods in centimetres for their scores. They check each other's measurements. The winner is the one with the most points after two rounds. ⬜P

Variation 2
Players take two cards and score the difference between the two rod lengths for those numbers.

71 **i** The children estimate first, then measure the lengths of each fishing rod, finally writing the lengths in order, from shortest to longest. [P]

ii *Game 2* A game for two players. The children each draw their own people fishing with fishing rods of different numbers of centimetres. They estimate the length of the fishing rods of each other's fishers, then measure them to see how close their estimates are. The winner is the one whose estimates are closest. [P]

72 The children measure each rod on pcm 28 and write its length alongside it. They investigate which pairs of fishing rods have a total length of 17 cm, and which pairs have a total length of 15 cm. They investigate which pairs are such that one rod is 2 cm longer than the other. [I][P][G]

Answers

71 **i** The lengths of the fishing rods in order, shortest to longest, are: 5 cm, 6 cm, 7 cm, 8 cm, 9 cm, 10 cm, 11 cm, 12 cm.

72 The lengths which have a total of:
17 cm are: (5, 12), (6, 11), (7, 10), (8, 9);
15 cm are: (5, 10), (6, 9), (7, 8).

The lengths which have a difference of:
2 cm are: (5, 7), (6, 8), (7, 9), (8, 10), (9, 11), (10, 12).

Shape games

Purposes
- To count the number of sides and corners of a 2-D shape.
- To recognise the names of 2-D shapes with three to eight sides.

73 *Game 1* A game for two players, each with counters of their own colour, using pcm 29 and a dice made from a blank cube, marked 3,4,5,6,7,8. Players take turns to throw the dice and match the score with a shape with the same number of sides, placing a counter on the shape (*see* pcm 29 for rules.) [P]

Variation 1
Only one counter is allowed on each shape.

Variation 2
Players throw a 1– 6 dice, then add two to the dice number, before matching this with the number of sides of a shape.

74 The children colour the shapes on pcm 29 according to their number of sides, e.g. three sides, red; four sides, green, etc. Then they write the name of each shape alongside it and the number of sides inside each shape. [I][P]

75 *Game 2* For two or more players, using sets of plastic or card 3-D shapes. Players sort the shapes into sets which have the same number of sides. They choose two or three of each shape, spread them out on a table, then play the game in 73 by placing counters on the shapes. [P][G]

76 *Game 3* For two or more players, using a set of plastic or card 2-D shapes. Players make a set of labels showing the names of shapes: triangle, square, rectangle, pentagon, hexagon, heptagon, octagon – two or three of each. They shuffle the labels and spread them out face down. They take turns to choose a label, read it and find a matching shape from a set of plastic or card 2-D shapes. [P][G]

Answers

74 Triangles (3 sides): shape 2;
rectangle (4 sides): shape 11;
square (4 equal sides): shape 3;
octagons (8 sides): shapes 1, 7;
pentagons (5 sides): shapes 4, 5;
hexagons (6 sides): shapes 6,8;
heptagons (7 sides): shapes 9,10.

Shape games

You need blank cube, counters (2 colours)

Game 1 A game for 2 players
- Make a dice by writing 3, 4, 5, 6, 7, 8 on the faces of a blank cube. Take turns to throw the dice.
- Put a counter on a shape with the same number of sides as your score. (You can put a counter on top of another.)
- The game is over when all shapes have at least 1 counter.
- The winner is the one with most counters showing.

▲ pcm 29, *page 59*

Number races

You will need
- copies of pcm 30
- 1–6 dice
- counters
- interlocking cubes
- base 10 materials

▲ **pcm 30**, *page 60*

Purposes
- To recognise the number of tens in a two-digit number.
- To recognise the number of units in a two-digit number.
- To recognise the nearest ten to a two-digit number.
- To recognise how far a two-digit number is from its nearest ten.

Game 1 A game for two players, each with a counter, using pcm 30, base 10 materials and a dice. Players take turns to throw the dice and move their counter a matching number of spaces, collecting base 10 longs to match the the number of tens in the number they land on (*see* pcm 30 for rules). **P**

Variation 1
Players collect base 10 ones to match the number of units in each number.

Variation 2
When players land on a number, they say which is its nearest ten, then collect a matching number of base 10 ones to represent the number of units to the nearest ten. For example, if you land on 42 you collect 2 cubes, if you land on 47 you collect 3 cubes.

Variation 3
Players use a pile of base ten materials. When they land on a two digit number they collect a matching number of base 10 pieces, exchanging them for longs and hundreds. At the end of the game, the winner is the player who has collected the most materials.

Variation 4
When players land on a two digit number they add the two digits together, and collect a number of base 10 pieces to match this total, or alternatively, to match the difference between the two digits.

78 Ask *How many numbers are there altogether on the board on pcm 30?* **I P** Ask the children to list them in order from smallest to largest, and to list their nearest ten alongside each.

79 The children invent their own race game, writing their own two digit **P G** or three digit numbers and inventing a rule for collecting base 10 materials.

Answers

78 There are 27 numbers altogether. In order, from smallest to largest (together with their nearest ten) they are:

11 (10),	24 (20),	45 (40 or 50),
13 (10),	26 (30),	48 (50),
15 (10 or 20),	28 (30),	49 (50),
17 (20),	30 (30),	51 (50),
19 (20),	31 (30),	54 (50),
22 (20),	34 (30),	56 (60),
	35 (30 or 40),	57 (60),
	37 (40),	58 (60),
	39 (40),	62 (60),
	40 (40),	63 (60).
	42 (40),	

Football games

Game 1 A game for 2 players

❏ Take turns to throw 2 dice.
❏ If the total matches a shirt number, put one
   of your counters on it and score a goal.
❏ Only 1 counter can go on each shirt.
❏ The winner is the first to score 7 goals.

Name .... **Date** ....

100 IDEAS for MATHS 5 –7 © Harper*Collins*Publishers Ltd 1996

Fishing games

You need 1–8 number cards, cm ruler

Game 1 A game for 2 players

❑ Shuffle a set of 1–8 number cards.
   Put them in a pile face down.

❑ Take a card each. Each put your card on the fisher
   with the matching number.

❑ Measure the length of both fishing rods, in centimetres.

❑ The winner of the round is the one whose fisher
   has the longest fishing rod.

❑ The winner is the one who wins most of 4 rounds.

| Name .... | Date .... |

100 IDEAS for MATHS 5 –7 © HarperCollins*Publishers* Ltd 1996

You need blank cube, counters (2 colours)

Shape games

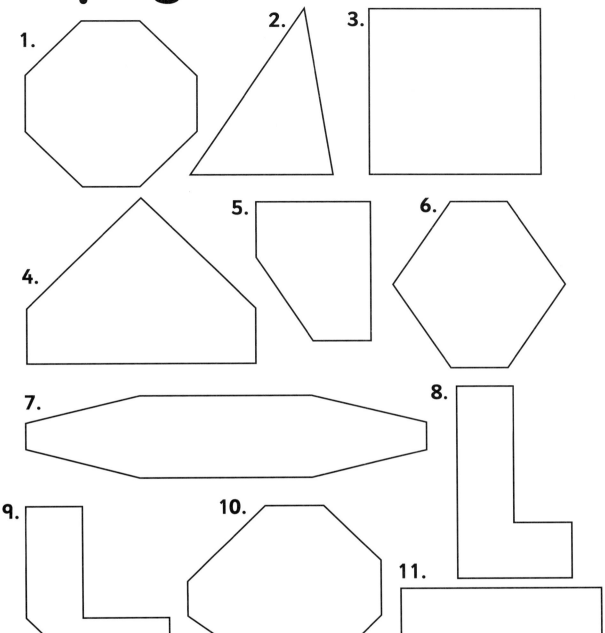

Game 1 A game for 2 players

❏ Make a dice by writing 3, 4, 5, 6, 7, 8 on the faces of a blank cube. Take turns to throw the dice.

❏ Put a counter on a shape with the same number of sides as your score. (You can put a counter on top of another.)

❏ The game is over when all shapes have at least 1 counter.

❏ The winner is the one with most counters showing.

Name .... Date ....

Number races

You need 1–6 dice, 2 counters (2 colours), base 10 materials

START	22	34	11	42	39	51

					30

54	13	45	62	24	58

37					

26	49	57	15	48	31

					19

FINISH	35	63	17	40	28	56

Game 1 A game for 2 players

❑ Place your counters on Start.
❑ Take turns to throw the dice and move your counter a matching number of spaces.
❑ Collect base 10 longs to match the tens in the numbers you land on.
❑ The game ends when the first player reaches Finish.
❑ The winner is the one who has collected most longs.

Name .... **Date** ....

Hit the target

You will need
- copies of pcm 31
- counters

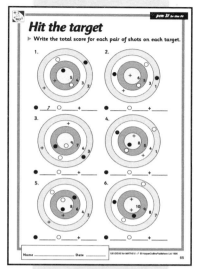

▲ **pcm 31**, *page 65*

Purposes
- To add two numbers (total up to 20).
- To work systematically.

80 The children write the total score for each pair of shots on each target |I| |P| on pcm 31.

Then ask:
▶ *Mark your own pairs of shots on each target, then find and record the scores.*

81 The children draw a large version of one of the targets on pcm 31 |P| |G| (or it can be enlarged on the photocopier). Using this and counters, they investigate what different scores are possible with two shots on the target.

Then ask:
▶ *Investigate different scores with three shots.*
▶ *Investigate ways of making the same score, e.g. ten, using the large targets.*

Answers

80 Target 1: (7,7,6); target 2: (4,8,9);
target 3: (10,15,9); target 4: (12,6,12);
target 5: (14,12,8); target 6: (17,15,20).

81 The possible two-shot scores on each target are:

target 1:
4: (2+2)   5: (2+3)
6: (2+4,3+3)   7: (2+5,3+4)
8: (3+5,4+4)   9: (4+5)
10: (5+5).

target 2:
2: (1+1)   4: (1+3)
6: (1+5,3+3)   7: (1+6)
8: (3+5)   9: (3+6)
10: (5+5)   11: (5+6)
12: (6+6).

target 3:
6: (3+3)   9: (3+6)
10: (3+7)   12: (3+9,6+6)
13: (6+7)   14: (7+7)
15: (6+9)   16: (7+9)
18: (9+9).

target 4:
2: (1+1)   5: (1+4)
6: (1+5)   8: (4+4)
9: (1+8,4+5)   10: (5+5)
12: (4+8)   13: (5+8)
16: (8+8).

target 5:
4: (2+2)   6: (2+4)
8: (2+6,4+4)   10: (2+8,4+6)
12: (4+8,6+6)   14: (6+8)
16: (8+8).

target 6:
14: (7+7)   15: (7+8)
16: (7+9,8+8)   17: (7+10,8+9)
18: (8+10,9+9) 19: (9+10)
20: (10+10).

The different possible three-shot scores on each target are:

target 1:
6: (2+2+2)   7: (2+2+3)
8: (2+2+4,2+3+3)
9: (2+2+5,2+3+4,3+3+3)
10: (2+3+5,2+2+4,3+3+4)
11: (2+4+5,3+3+5,3+4+4)
12: (2+5+5,3+4+5,4+4+4)
13: (3+5+5,4+4+5)
14: (4+5+5)   15: (5+5+5).

target 2:
3: (1+1+1)   5: (1+1+3)
7: (1+1+5,1+3+3) 8: (1+1+6)
9: (1+3+5,3+3+3) 10: (1+3+6)
11: (1+5+5,3+3+5)
12: (1+5+6,3+3+6)
13: (1+6+6,3+5+5)
14: (3+5+6)   15: (3+6+6,5+5+5)
16: (5+5+6)   18: (6+6+6).

target 3:
9: (3+3+3)   12: (3+3+6)
13: (3+3+7)   15: (3+3+9,3+6+6)
16: (3+6+7)   17: (3+7+7)
18: (3+6+9,6+6+6)
19: (3+7+9,6+6+7) 20: (6+7+7)
21: (3+9+9,6+6+9,7+7+7)
22: (6+7+9)
23: (7+7+9)   24: (6+9+9)
25: (7+9+9)   27: (9+9+9).

target 4:
3: (1+1+1)   6: (1+1+4)
7: (1+1+5)   9: (1+4+4)
10: (1+1+8,1+4+5)
11: (1+5+5)   12: (4+4+4)
13: (1+4+8,4+4+5)
14: (1+5+8,4+5+5)
15: (5+5+5)   16: (4+4+8)
17: (1+8+8,4+5+8)
18: (5+5+8)   20: (4+8+8)
21: (5+8+8)   24: (8+8+8).

target 5:
6: (2+2+2)   8: (2+2+4)
10: (2+2+6,2+4+4)
12: (2+2+8,2+4+6,4+4+4)
14: (2+4+8,2+6+6,4+4+6)
16: (2+6+8,4+4+8,4+6+6)
18: (2+8+8,4+6+8,6+6+6)
20: (4+8+8,6+6+8)
22: (6+8+8)   24: (8+8+8).

target 6:
21: (7+7+7)   22: (7+7+8)
23: (7+7+9,7+8+8)
24: (7+7+10,7+8+9,8+8+8)
25: (7+8+10,7+9+9,8+8+9)
26: (7+9+10,8+8+10,8+9+9)
27: (7+10+10,8+9+10,9+9+9)
28: (8+10+10,9+9+10)
29: (9+10+10)   30: (10+10+10).

Square targets

You will need
- copies of pcm 32
- counters

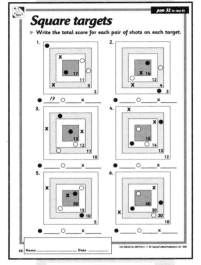

▲ **pcm 32**, *page 66*

Purposes
- To add a single- and two-digit number.
- To add two two-digit numbers.
- To work systematically.

82 The children write the total score for each pair of shots on each target ⬚I⬚ ⬚P⬚ on pcm 32.

Then ask them to:
▸ *Mark your own pairs of shots on each target, then find and record the scores.*

83 The children draw a large version of one of the targets on pcm 32 ⬚I⬚ ⬚P⬚ ⬚G⬚ (or it an be enlarged on the photocopier). Using this and counters, they investigate what different scores are possible with two shots on the target.

Then ask them to:
▸ *Investigate different scores with three shots.*

Answers

82 Target 1: (19, 14, 14)
target 2: (19, 16, 20)
target 3: (24, 23, 22)
target 4: (27, 29, 26)
target 5: (30, 30, 25)
target 6: (50, 60, 40).

83 The possible two-shot scores on each target are:
target 1:
4: (2+2)	5: (2+3)
6: (3+3)	13: (2+11)
14: (3+11)	19: (2+17)
20: (3+17)	22: (11+11)
28: (11+17)	34: (17+17).

target 2:
6: (3+3)	7: (3+4)
8: (4+4)	15: (3+12)
16: (4+12)	19: (3+16)
20: (4+16)	24: (12+12)
28: (12+16)	32: (16+16).

target 3:
20: (10+10)
21: (10+11)
22:(10+12,11+11)
23: (10+13,11+12)
24: (11+13,12+12)
25: (12+13)
26: (13+13).

target 4:
24: (12+12)	25: (12+13)
26: (12+14,13+13)	27: (12+15,13+14)
28: (13+15,14+14)	29: (14+15)
30: (15+15).	

target 5:
10: (5+5)	15: (5+10)
20: (5+15,10+10)	25: (5+20,10+15)
30: (10+20,15+15)	
35: (15+20)	40:(20+20).

target 6:
20: (10+10)	30:(10+20)
40: (10+30,20+20)	50: (10+40,20+30)
60: (20+40,30+30)	
70: (30+40)	80:(40+40).

The possible three-shot scores on each target are:
target 1:
6: (2+2+2)	7:(2+2+3)
8: (2+3+3)	9:(3+3+3)
15: (2+2+11)	16:(2+3+11)
17: (3+3+11)	21: (2+2+17)
22: (2+3+17)	23: (3+3+17)
24: (2+11+11)	25: (3+11+11)

30: (2+11+17)	31: (3+11+17)
33: (11+11+11)	36: (2+17+17)
37: (3+17+17)	39: (11+11+17)
45: (11+17+17)	51: (17+17+17).

target 2:
9: (3+3+3)	10: (3+3+4)
11: (3+4+4)	12: (4+4+4)
18: (3+3+12)	19: (3+4+12)
20: (4+4+12)	22: (3+3+16)
23: (3+4+16)	24: (4+4+16)
27: (3+12+12)	28: (4+12+12)
31: (3+12+16)	32: (4+12+16)
35: (3+16+16)	
36:(4+16+16,12+12+12)
40: (12+12+16)
44: (12+16+16)
48: (16+16+16).

target 3:
30: (10+10+10)
31: (10+10+11)
32: (10+10+12,10+11+11)
33: (10+10+13,10+11+12,11+11+11)
34: (10+11+13,10+12+12,11+11+12)
35: (10+12+13,11+11+13,11+12+12)
36: (10+13+13,11+12+13,12+12+12)
37: (11+13+13,12+12+13)
38: (12+13+13)   39: (13+13+13).

target 4:
36: (12+12+12)	37: (12+12+13)
38: (12+12+14,12+13+13)
40: (12+13+15,12+14+14,13+13+14)
41: (12+14+15,13+13+15,13+14+14)
42: (12+15+15,13+14+15,14+14+14)
43: (13+15+15,14+14+15)
44: (14+15+15)	45: (15+15+15).

target 5:
15: (5+5+5)	20: (5+5+10)
25: (5+5+15,5+10+10)
30: (5+5+20,5+10+15,10+10+10)
35: (5+10+20,5+15+15,10+10+15)
40: (5+15+20,10+10+20,10+15+15)
45: (5+20+20,10+15+20,15+15+15)
50: (10+20+20,15+15+20)
55: (15+20+20)	60: (20+20+20).

target 6:
30: (10+10+10)	40: (10+10+20)
50: (10+10+30,10+20+20)
60: (10+20+30,10+10+40,20+20+20)
70: (10+20+40,10+30+30,20+20+30)
80: (10+30+40,20+20+40,20+30+30)
90: (10+40+40,20+30+40,30+30+30)
100: (20+40+40,30+30+40)
110: (30+40+40)   120: (40+40+40).

Ring-a-number

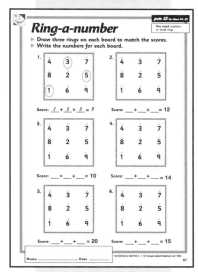

▲ **pcm 33**, *page 67*

Purposes
- To add three single-digit numbers.
- To find three single-digit numbers with a given total.
- To work systematically.

84 The children draw rings round three numbers on each board on pcm 33 to match the given scores. Using counters or small rings, they investigate how many different ways there are of obtaining each score on each board. `I P`

Ask them to:
▸ *Investigate what different scores are possible on each board.*

85 More activities for pcm 33: `I P G`
▸ *Investigate different ways of scoring, say twelve, with two rings on each board.*
▸ *Investigate different ways of scoring other totals with two rings on each board.*

86 The children draw a large version of a blank board on pcm 33 and write in a different set of numbers. Using this and counters investigate similar questions to those above. `P G`

Answers
84 The ways of obtaining each score on each board are:
board 1: (1,2,6), (1,3,5), (1,2,6).
board 2: (1,2,9), (1,3,8), (1,4,7), (1,5,6), (2,3,7), (2,4,6), (3,4,5).
board 3: (1,2,7), (1,3,6), (1,4,5), (2,3,5).

board 4: (1,4,9), (1,5,8), (1,6,7), (2,3,9), (2,4,8), (2,5,7), (3,4,7), (3,5,6).
board 5: (3,8,9), (4,7,9), (5,6,9), (5,7,8).
board 6: (1,5,9), (1,6,8), (2,4,9), (2,5,8), (2,4,8), (3,4,8), (3,5,7), (4,5,6).

85 The different possible scores range from 6 to 24. The number of different ways of obtaining each score are:

score:	6	7	8	9	10	11	12	13	14	15	16	17	18	19	20	21	22	23	24
ways:	1	1	2	3	4	5	7	7	8	8	8	7	7	5	4	3	2	1	1

With two rings, the number of different ways of obtaining each score are:

score:	3	4	5	6	7	8	9	10	11	12	13	14	15	16	17
ways:	1	1	2	2	3	3	4	4	4	3	3	2	2	1	1

Two darts

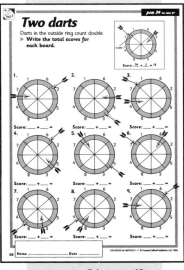

▲ **pcm 34**, *page 68*

Purposes
- To double a single-digit number.
- To add two numbers (total up to 20).
- To work systematically.

87 The children write the total score for each pair of darts on each board on pcm 34. `I P`

Then ask them to:
▸ *Mark your own pairs of darts on each target and find the scores.*

88 The children draw a large version of one of the boards on pcm 34 (or it can be enlarged on the photocopier). Using this and counters, they investigate different ways of achieving the same score with two darts. (They can use the same number twice.) For example, ways of achieving 8 are: 1 and 7, 2 and 6, 3 and 5, 4 and 4, 6 and double 1, 4 and double 2, 2 and double 3. `I P`

Then ask them to:
▸ *Investigate what different scores are possible with two darts.*
▸ *Investigate what different scores are possible with three darts.*
▸ *If the darts in the outside ring count treble, investigate different possible scores.*

89 The children create their own dart boards, using circular sheets   P G
of paper, and investigate different one-dart, two-dart and three-dart scores.

90 Look at a real dart board with the children. Discuss the doubles,   P G
trebles, the inner-bull and outer-bull. Ask them to investigate different
possible scores and different ways of achieving the same score.

Answers

87 1. 11   2. 8   3. 6
4. 17   5. 11   6. 20
7. 19   8. 16   9. 19.

88 Ways of achieving the
same score with two darts
2: (1+1) 3:(1+2,1+D1)
4: (1+3,2+2,2+D1)
5: (1+4,2+3,3+D1,1+D2)
6: (1+5,2+4,3+3,4+D1,
2+D2,D1+D2)
7: (1+6,2+5,3+4,5+D1,
3+D2,1+D3)
8: (1+7,2+6,3+5,4+4,
6+D1,4+D2,2+D3,
D1+D3,D2+D2)
9: (1+8,2+7,3+6,4+5,
7+D1,5+D2,3+D3,1+D4)
10: (2+8,3+7,4+6,8+D1,
6+D2,4+D3,2+D4,
D1+D4,D2+D3)
11: (3+8,4+7,5+6,7+D2,
5+D3,3+D4,1+D5)
12: (4+8,5+7,6+6,
8+D2,6+D3,4+D4,
2+D5,D1+D5,D3+D3)
13: (5+8,6+7,7+D3,
5+D4,3+D5,1+D6)
14: (6+8,7+7,8+D3,
6+D4,4+D5,2+D6,
D1+D6,D4+D3)
15: (7+8,7+D4,5+D5,
3+D6,1+D7)
16: (8+8,8+D4,6+D5,
4+D6,2+D7,D1+D7,
D5+D3,D4+D4)
17: (7+D5,5+D6,3+D7,
1+D8)
18: (8+D5,6+D6,4+D7,
2+D8,D1+D8,D6+D3,
D5+D4)
19: (7+D6,5+D7,3+D8)
20: (8+D6,6+D7,4+D8,
D7+D3,D6+D4,D5+D5)
21: (7+D7,5+D8)
22: (8+D7,6+D8,D8+D3,
D7+D4,D5+D6)

23: (7+D8)
24: (8+D8,D8+D4,
D5+D7,D6+D6)
26: (D5+D8,D7+D6)
28: (D8+D6,D7+D7)
30: (D8+D7)
32: (D8+D8).

With three darts there are
numerous ways of
obtaining the same score.
The following are possible
totals, and one way
of achieving each total:
3: (1,1,1)
4: (1,1,2)
5: (1,1,3)
6: (1,1,4)
7: (1,1,5)
8: (1,1,6)
9: (1,1,7)
10: (1,1,8)
11: (1,2,8)
12: (1,3,8)
13: (1,4,8)
14: (1,6,7)
15: (1,6,8)
16: (1,7,8)
17: (1,8,8)
18: (2,8,8)
19: (3,8,8)
20: (4,8,8)
21: (5,8,8)
22: (6,8,8)
23: (7,8,8)
24: (8,8,8)
25: (D6,D6,1)
26: (D6,D6,2)
27: (D6,D6,3)
28: (D6,D6,4)
29: (D6,D6,5)
30: (D6,D6,6)
31: (D6,D6,7)
32: (D6,D6,8)
33: (D7,D7,5)
34: (D7,D7,6)
35: (D7,D7,7)
36: (D7,D7,8)
37: (D8,D8,5)
38: (D8,D8,6)

39: (D8,D8,7)
40: (D8,D8,8)
42: (D8,D8,D5)
44: (D8,D8,D6)
46: (D8,D8,D7)
48: (D8,D8,D8).
If darts in the outer ring
count treble, the scores
1 to 24 are still possible.
Other possible scores
greater than 24 are:
25: (T4,T4,1)
26: (T4,T4,2)
27: (T4,T4,3)
28: (T4,T4,4)
29: (T4,T4,5)
30: (T4,T4,6)
31: (T4,T4,7)
32: (T4,T4,8)
33: (T5,T5,3)
34: (T5,T5,4)
35: (T5,T5,5)
36: (T5,T5,6)
37: (T5,T5,7)
38: (T5,T5,8)
39: (T6,T6,3)
40: (T6,T6,4)
41: (T6,T6,5)
42: (T6,T6,6)
43: (T6,T6,7)
44: (T6,T6,8)
45: (T7,T7,3)
46: (T7,T7,4)
47: (T7,T7,5)
48: (T7,T7,6)
49: (T7,T7,7)
50: (T7,T7,8)
51: (T8,T8,3)
52: (T8,T8,4)
53: (T8,T8,5)
54: (T8,T8,6)
55: (T8,T8,7)
56: (T8,T8,8)
57: (T8,T8,T3)
60: (T8,T8,T4)
63: (T8,T8,T5)
66: (T8,T8,T6)
69: (T8,T8,T7)
72: (T8,T8,T8).

Hit the target

▶ Write the total score for each pair of shots on each target.

1.

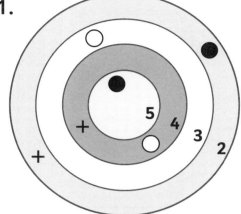

● ____7____ ○ _____ + _____

2.

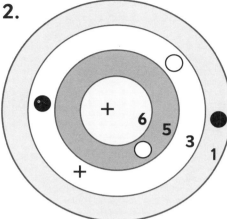

● _____ ○ _____ + _____

3.

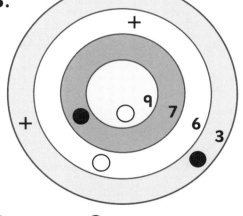

● _____ ○ _____ + _____

4.

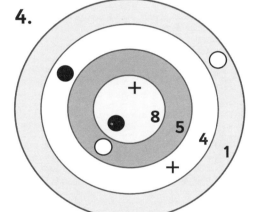

● _____ ○ _____ + _____

5.

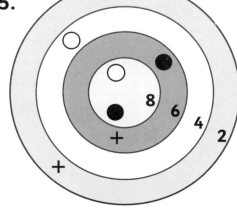

● _____ ○ _____ + _____

6.

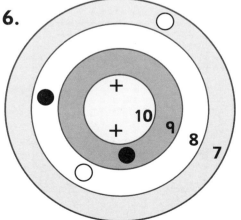

● _____ ○ _____ + _____

Name .... Date ....

100 IDEAS for MATHS 5 –7 © HarperCollins*Publishers* Ltd 1996

Square targets

▶ Write the total score for each pair of shots on each target.

1.
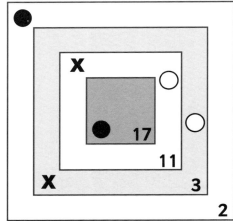

● __*19*__ ○ _____ X _____

2.
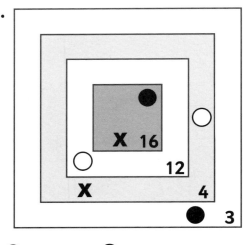

● _____ ○ _____ X _____

3.
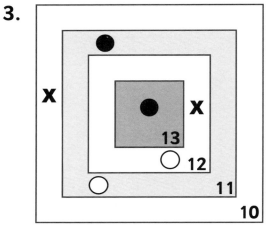

● _____ ○ _____ X _____

4.

● _____ ○ _____ X _____

5.
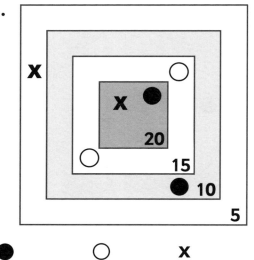

● _____ ○ _____ X _____

6.
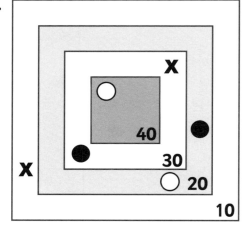

● _____ ○ _____ X _____

100 IDEAS for MATHS 5 –7 © HarperCollins*Publishers* Ltd 1996

66 | **Name** .... **Date** ....

Ring-a-number

You need counters or small rings

▶ Draw three rings on each board to match the scores.
▶ Write the numbers for each board.

1.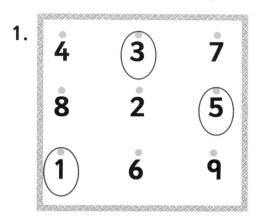

4	③	7
8	2	⑤
①	6	9

Score: $\underline{\;1\;} + \underline{\;3\;} + \underline{\;5\;} = 9$

2.

4	3	7
8	2	5
1	6	9

Score: ___ + ___ + ___ = 12

3.

4	3	7
8	2	5
1	6	9

Score: ___ + ___ + ___ = 10

4.

4	3	7
8	2	5
1	6	9

Score: ___ + ___ + ___ = 14

5.

4	3	7
8	2	5
1	6	9

Score: ___ + ___ + ___ = 20

6.

4	3	7
8	2	5
1	6	9

Score: ___ + ___ + ___ = 15

Name .... Date ....

Two darts

Darts in the outside ring count double.

▶ **Write the total scores for each board.**

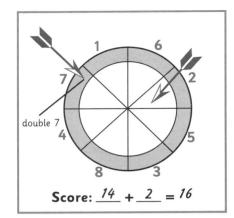

double 7

Score: _14_ + _2_ = 16

1.

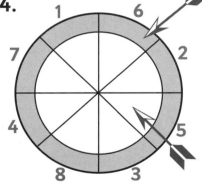

Score: ___ + ___ =

2.

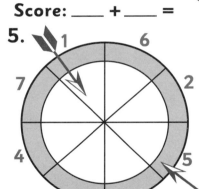

Score: ___ + ___ =

3.

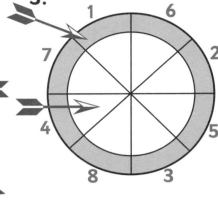

Score: ___ + ___ =

4.

Score: ___ + ___ =

5.

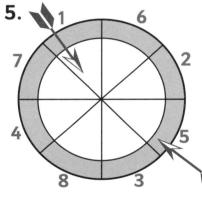

Score: ___ + ___ =

6.

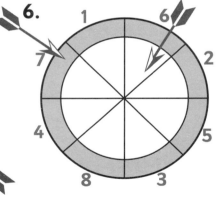

Score: ___ + ___ =

7.

Score: ___ + ___ =

8.

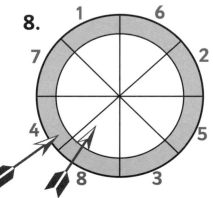

Score: ___ + ___ =

9.

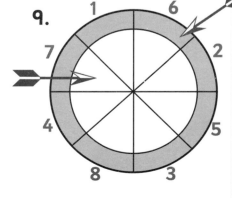

Score: ___ + ___ =

Name .... Date ....

100 IDEAS for MATHS 5 –7 © HarperCollins*Publishers* Ltd 1996

Shapes

Purposes
- To recognise and name squares, triangles, rectangles and circles.
- To sort 2-D shapes according to their numbers of sides and corners.
- To construct and interpret a block graph.

91 The children colour the shapes on pcm 35: the squares red, | I | P |
the triangles blue, the rectangles green, the circles yellow and the other
shapes pink. Using the outline block graph on pcm 7, they draw and
colour the block graph to show how many there are of each shape.

Ask them:
- ▸ *What does the block graph show about the shapes?*
- ▸ *Count the number of sides of each shape and write the number inside the shape.*
- ▸ *How many shapes have one side, two sides, three sides ...?*
- ▸ *How many corners does each shape have?*

92 The children draw their own set of shapes with different numbers | P |
of sides. They colour them according to their number of sides and write
the number of sides inside them.

93 The children, in pairs, sort a set of 2-D shapes into sets with the same | P |
number of sides.

Ask them:
- ▸ *Name as many of the shapes as possible.*
- ▸ *Make labels, one for each shape: square, triangle, rectangle, circle,*
  pentagon, etc., and add them to the sets of shapes.

Answers
91 There are four squares (red), five rectangles (green), three circles (yellow), and five triangles (blue). The other two shapes (pink) are one oval and one pentagon.

Four shapes have 1 side (circles, oval). No shapes have 2 sides. Five shapes have 3 sides (triangles). Nine shapes have 4 sides (squares, rectangles). One shape has 5 sides (pentagon).

Circles and oval (four) have 0 corners. Triangles (five) have 3 corners. Squares and rectangles (nine) have 4 corners. Pentagon (one) has 5 corners.

You will need
- copies of pcm 35
- sets of plastic/card 2-D shapes
- outline block graph (pcm 7)

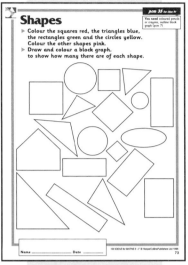

▲ pcm 35, *page 73*

You will need
- copies of pcm 36
- Geoboards, preferably 3×3, or 3×3 sections of larger Geoboards
- rubber bands

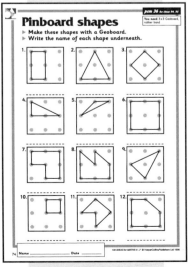

▲ pcm 36, *page 74*

Pinboard shapes

Purposes
- To recognise and name squares, triangles, rectangles, pentagons and hexagons.
- To sort 2-D shapes according to various criteria.
- To construct 2-D shapes using a Geoboard.

94 **i** The children make the shapes on pcm 36 with rubber bands | I | P |
and 3 x 3 Geoboards, then write the name of each shape underneath.

Ask them:
- ▸ *How many of each shape are there?*
- ▸ *Colour the shapes so that all the triangles are one colour, all the squares*
  another colour, and so on.

ii Photocopy pcm 36, enlarged, onto card. Ask the children to cut out | I | P |
the shapes and sort them.

95 More questions for pcm 36: | I | P |
Investigate the properties of the shapes:
- ▸ *How many sides does each shape have?*
- ▸ *How many corners does each shape have?*
- ▸ *How many pins are on the boundary of each shape?*

▸ *How many pins are inside each shape?*
▸ *How many pins are outside each shape?*

96 The children make other shapes on a Geoboard. They make different squares and triangles. Ask, *How many different squares and triangles are possible?* `I` `P`

97 **A game for two,** using the cut-out shapes from 94 spread out so that both players can see them. Player A describes one of the shapes. Player B has to decide which shape is being described. Then they swap roles. `I` `P`

Variation Player A thinks of a shape. Player B has to find out which one of the cut-out shapes it is by asking questions, to which the only answer can be 'Yes' or 'No'. Player B sorts the shapes in response to the answers, until the shape is deduced. They swap roles.

Answers

94 The shapes are:
1. rectangle   2. triangle
3. square   4. triangle
5. triangle   6. square
7. hexagon   8. hexagon
9. triangle   10. square
11. pentagon
12. pentagon.
There are four triangles, three squares, one rectangle, two pentagons, two hexagons.

95 The number of sides on each shape are:
1, 3, 6, 10: 4; 2, 4, 5, 9: 3; 7, 8: 6; 11, 12: 5.
The number of corners on each shape are:
1, 3, 6, 10: 4; 2, 4, 5, 9: 3; 7, 8: 6; 11, 12: 5.

The number of pins on the boundary of each shape are:
1.6   2.4   3.4   4.4
5.3   6.8   7.8   8.8
9.3 10.4 11.5 12.7.

The number of pins inside each shape are:
1.0   2.1   3.1   4.0
5.0   6.1   7.0   8.0
9.1 10.0 11.0 12.1.

The number of pins outside each shape are:
1.3   2.4   3.4   4.5
5.6   6.0   7.1   8.1
9.5 10.5 11.4 12.1.

96 Three different squares are possible, and eight different triangles:

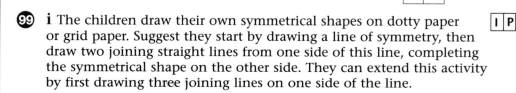

Symmetry

Purposes
● To recognise which shapes have symmetry.
● To draw the second side of a symmetrical shape when given one side.
● To use a mirror to help explore symmetrical patterns.
● To find one half and one quarter of a quantity.

98 Explain that the dotted lines on pcm 37 are lines of symmetry. (Ensure that the children understand the term.) The children draw the other half of each shape. Suggest they use a mirror to help. `I` `P`

Then ask:
▸ *Colour each half of the symmetrical shapes a different colour.*
▸ *Cut out the completed shapes, then fold them along the line of symmetry to show that one half matches the other.*
▸ *Draw pairs of symmetrical eyes on some of the shapes.*

99 **i** The children draw their own symmetrical shapes on dotty paper or grid paper. Suggest they start by drawing a line of symmetry, then draw two joining straight lines from one side of this line, completing the symmetrical shape on the other side. They can extend this activity by first drawing three joining lines on one side of the line. `I` `P`

You will need
● copies of pcm 37
● unbreakable mirrors
● 1 cm squared dotty or grid paper

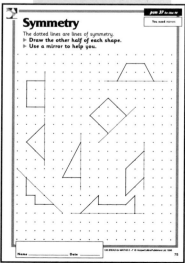

▲ **pcm 37,** *page 75*

ii The children draw their own symmetrical faces, by drawing a symmetrical shape, then adding pairs of eyes and ears, for example.

100 **i** The children investigate squares and their different lines of symmetry. Suggest they draw several squares, all the same size, on square dotty or grid paper, then draw a different line of symmetry on each square. Ask, *How many possible lines of symmetry does a square have?*

ii Ask them to draw some triangles which have a line of symmetry. I P

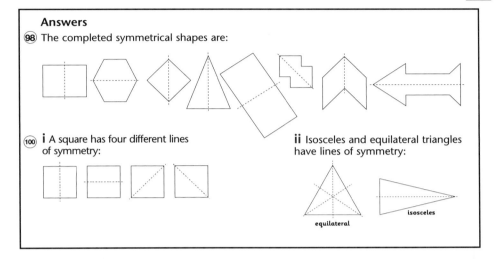

Answers

98 The completed symmetrical shapes are:

100 **i** A square has four different lines of symmetry:

ii Isosceles and equilateral triangles have lines of symmetry:

equilateral

isosceles

Circle patterns

You will need
- copies of pcm 38

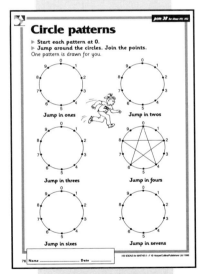

▲ **pcm 38**, *page 75*

Purposes
- To recognise patterns in shapes and numbers.
- To recognise sequences in numbers.
- To consolidate multiplication sequences: x2, x3, etc.

101 The children draw lines linking the numbers on the circles on pcm 38, starting each pattern at 0 and jumping round the circles as described. Ask, *Do you always finish back where you started?* I P

Then ask:
- *Investigate what patterns and shapes you have drawn.*
- *Colour the shapes to highlight the patterns.*

102 More activities for pcm 38: P G
- *Investigate what happens if you start at a different position, instead of 0. For example, draw the 'jump in threes' pattern starting at 0, then 1, then 2, and so on.*
- *Investigate what happens if you jump in other numbers, e.g. fives, eights, nines.*
- *Investigate which jumps make the same patterns.*

103 Ask the children to write the numbers in the x 2 table in sequence, i.e. 2, 4, 6, 8, 10, 12, 14, 16, 18, 20; then to write the units digits in the x 2 table sequence, i.e. 2, 4, 6, 8, 0, 2, 4, 6, 8, 0. I P G

Ask them:
- *What patterns can you see in this sequence?*
- *Compare this with the numbers which are joined in order in the 'jumping in twos' pattern, starting at 0.*
- *Extend this to the x 3 table, etc.*

Answers

101 The completed drawings are:

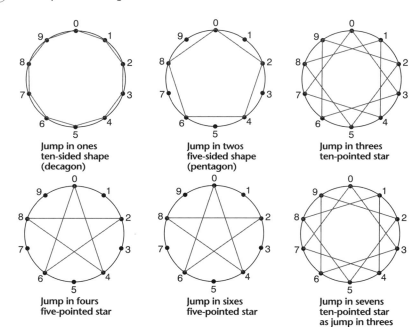

Jump in ones
ten-sided shape
(decagon)

Jump in twos
five-sided shape
(pentagon)

Jump in threes
ten-pointed star

Jump in fours
five-pointed star

Jump in sixes
five-pointed star

Jump in sevens
ten-pointed star
as jump in threes

102 If you start at different positions, the same shapes and patterns are created but sometimes they have been rotated. The patterns for jumping in ones, threes, sevens, nines remain the same.

Other patterns are:

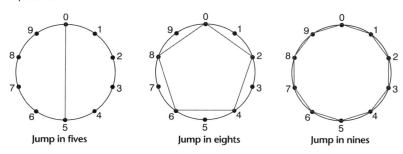

Jump in fives

Jump in eights

Jump in nines

103 Identical patterns are produced by jumps in ones and nines; by jumps in twos and eights; by jumps in threes and sevens; by jumps in fours and sixes.
Note that these pairs have jump numbers which add up to ten.

The sequences of the units digits are:

x 2:	2	4	6	8	0	2	4	6	8	0 (repeats 2, 4, 6, 8, 0 in fives);
x 3:	3	6	9	2	5	8	1	4	7	0 (one of each digit);
x 4:	4	8	2	6	0	4	8	2	6	0 (repeats 4, 8, 2, 6, 0 in fives);
x 5:	5	0	5	0	5	0	5	0	5	0 (repeats 5, 0 in twos);
x 6:	6	2	8	4	0	6	2	8	4	0 (repeats 6, 2, 8, 4, 0 in fives);
x 7:	7	4	1	8	5	2	9	6	3	0 (one of each digit);
x 8:	8	6	4	2	0	8	6	4	2	0 (repeats 8, 6, 4, 2, 0 in fives);
x 9:	9	8	7	6	5	4	3	2	1	0 (one of each digit in descending order).

Shapes

pcm **35** for idea 91

You need coloured pencils or crayons, outline block graph (pcm 7)

▶ Colour the squares red, the triangles blue, the rectangles green and the circles yellow. Colour the other shapes pink.

▶ Draw and colour a block graph. to show how many there are of each shape.

Name .... Date ....

100 IDEAS for MATHS 5–7 © HarperCollins*Publishers* Ltd 1996

Pinboard shapes

You need 3 x 3 Geoboard, rubber band

▶ Make these shapes with a Geoboard.
▶ Write the name of each shape underneath.

1.
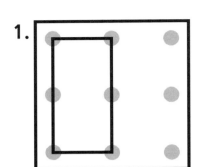

2.
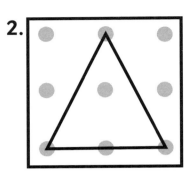

3.
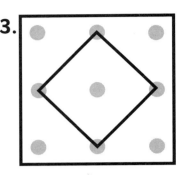

4.
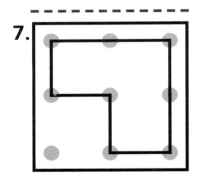

5.
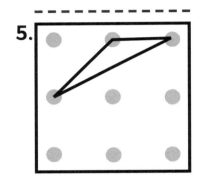

6.
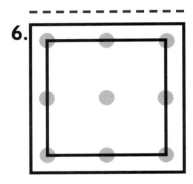

7.
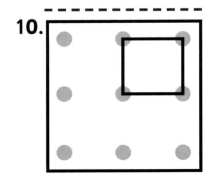

8.
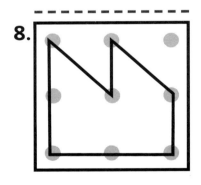

9.
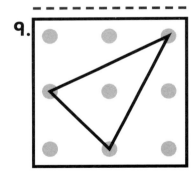

10.
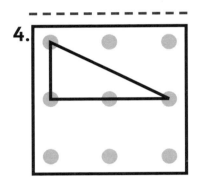

11.
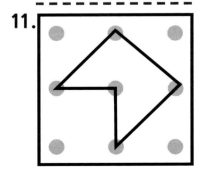

12.
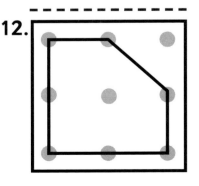

Name .... **Date** ....

100 IDEAS for MATHS 5 –7 © HarperCollins*Publishers* Ltd 1996

Symmetry

You need mirrors

The dotted lines are lines of symmetry.

▶ **Draw the other half of each shape.**

▶ **Use a mirror to help you.**

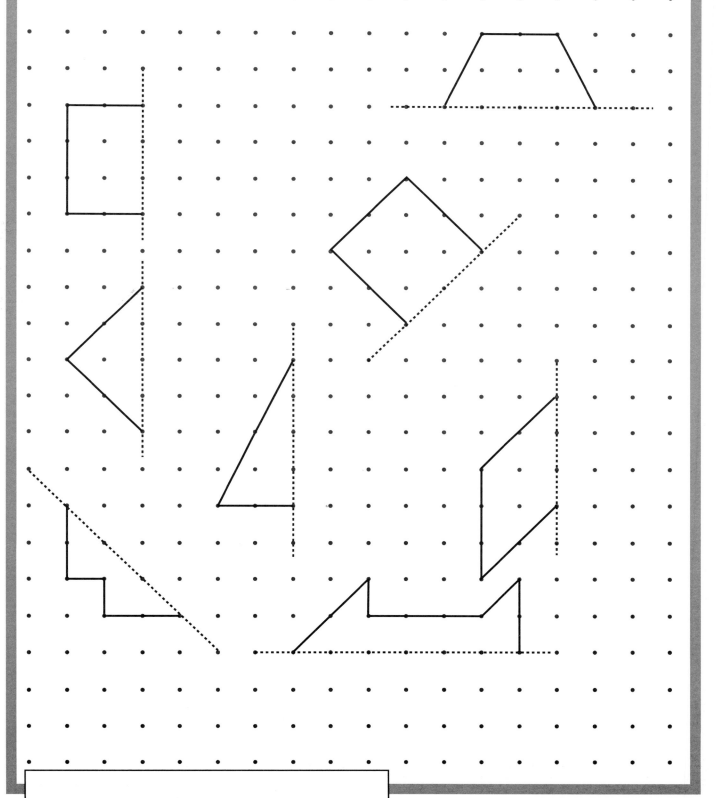

Name .... Date ....

Circle patterns

▶ **Start each pattern at 0.**
▶ **Jump around the circles. Join the points.**
One pattern is drawn for you.

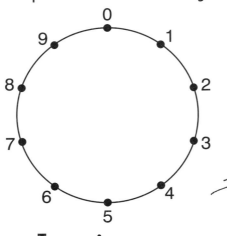

Jump in ones

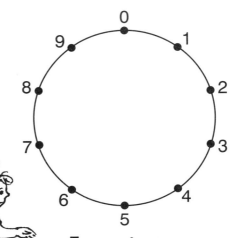

Jump in twos

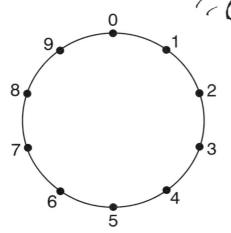

Jump in threes

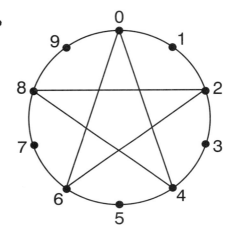

Jump in fours

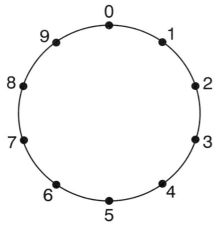

Jump in sixes

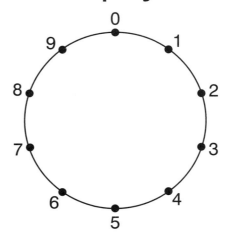

Jump in sevens

100 IDEAS for MATHS 5 –7 © HarperCollins*Publishers* Ltd 1996

Name .... **Date** ....

Abacus beads

Purposes
- To consolidate an understanding of place value in three-digit numbers.
- To order three-digit numbers.
- To add a number of tens, units or hundreds to a three-digit number.

(104) On pcm 39, the children write the numbers shown by the beads under each abacus 1–6. Then they draw beads to show the numbers under each abacus 7–12. `I | P`

Ask these questions about abaci 1-6:
- ▸ *Which is the smallest number? Which is the largest?*
- ▸ *Which number has the most units beads? Which has the fewest?*
- ▸ *Which number has the most tens beads? Which has the fewest?*
- ▸ *Which number has the most hundreds beads? Which has the fewest?*
- ▸ *Write the six numbers in order, from smallest to largest.*
- ▸ *Which number has the most beads altogether? Which has the fewest?*

Repeat all of the above questions for abaci 7–12.
Repeat all of the activities for all 12 numbers considered together.

(105) More activities for pcm 39: `I | P`
- ▸ *Investigate what new numbers are created if 20 is added to each number.*
- ▸ *Add other numbers to each, e.g. 5, 200, 130.*
- ▸ *Investigate what new numbers are created if 100 is taken away from each.*

Note
The children can use a spike abacus and beads to help with these activities.

(106) Further activities for pcm 39: `I | P`
- ▸ *What number is shown if each spike is filled up to the top?*
- ▸ *Look at the first number, 174. Investigate how many beads need to be added for each spike to reach the top. Investigate what three-digit number needs to be added to reach the top of all three spikes.*
- ▸ *Try the same activity for the other numbers.*

Sidebar

You will need
- copies of pcm 39
- spike abacus and beads (optional)

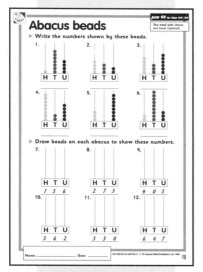

▲ **pcm 39**, *page 79*

Answers

(104) The numbers are:
1. 174, 2. 432, 3. 536,
4. 825, 5. 308, 6. 293.
The abacus beads are:

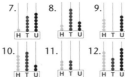

Abaci 1–6:
Smallest number: 1. 174,
largest: 4. 825.
Most units beads: 5. 308,
fewest units beads: 2. 432.
Most tens beads:
6. 293, fewest tens beads:
5. 308. Most hundreds
beads: 4. 825, fewest
hundreds beads: 1. 174.
Numbers in order are:
174, 293, 308, 432, 536, 825.
Most beads altogether:
4. 825 (15), fewest beads
altogether 2. 432 (9).

Abaci 7–12:
Smallest number: 7. 156,
largest number: 12. 647.
Most units beads: 12. 647,
fewest units beads: 11. 330.
Most tens beads: 8. 273,
fewest tens beads: 9. 405.

Most hundreds beads:
12. 647,
fewest hundreds beads: 7.
156.
Numbers in order are:
156, 273, 330, 405, 562, 647.
Most beads altogether:
12. 647 (17),
fewest beads altogether
11. 330 (6).

All 12 numbers together:
Smallest: 7. 156,
largest: 4. 825.
Most units beads: 5. 308,
fewest units beads: 11. 330.
Most tens beads: 6. 293,
fewest tens beads: 5. 308
and 9. 405.
Most hundreds beads: 4. 825,
fewest hundreds beads: 7. 156.
Numbers in order are:
156, 174, 273, 293, 308,
330, 405, 432, 536, 562,
647, 825.
Most beads altogether:
12. 647 (17),
fewest beads altogether:
11. 330 (6).

(105) If 20 is added to each,
the new numbers are:
1. 194, 2. 452, 3. 556,
4. 845, 5. 328, 6. 313,
7. 176, 8. 293, 9. 425,

---

10. 582, 11. 350, 12. 667.
If five is added to each,
the new numbers are:
1. 179, 2. 437, 3. 541,
4. 830, 5. 313, 6. 298,
7. 161, 8. 278, 9. 410,
10. 567, 11. 335,
12. 652.

If 200 is added to each,
the new numbers are:
1. 374, 2. 632, 3. 736,
4. 1025, 5. 508, 6. 493,
7. 356, 8. 473, 9. 605,
10. 762, 11. 530, 12. 847.

If 130 is added to each,
the new numbers are:
1. 304, 2. 562, 3. 666,
4. 955, 5. 438, 6. 423,
7. 286, 8. 403, 9. 535,
10. 692, 11. 460, 12. 777.

If 100 is taken away from
each, the new numbers are:
1. 74, 2. 332, 3. 436, 4. 725,
5. 208, 6. 193, 7. 56, 8. 173,
9. 305, 10. 462, 11. 230,
12. 547.

(106) To reach the top (999),
the numbers which have
to be added are:
1. 825, 2. 567, 3. 463,
4. 174, 5. 691, 6. 706,
7. 843, 8. 726, 9. 594,
10. 437, 11. 669, 12. 352.

Abacus

Purposes
- To consolidate an understanding of place value in three-digit numbers.
- To order three-digit numbers.
- To investigate the creation of different three-digit numbers on an abacus with a fixed number of beads.
- To work systematically.

You will need
- copies of pcm 40
- counters
- spike abacus and beads (optional)
- sets of 0–9 number cards
- interlocking cubes

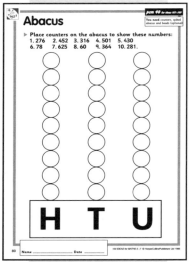

▲ **pcm 40**, *page 80*

107 The children place counters on the abacus on pcm 40 to show the numbers listed. [I] [P]

Note The children can record the positions of the counters by drawing beads on the blank abaci on pcm 40. They write the numbers shown by the beads under each abacus.
More questions for pcm 40:
- ▶ *Which number is the smallest? Which is the largest?*
- ▶ *Which number has the most units beads? Which has the fewest?*
- ▶ *Which number has the most tens beads? Which has the fewest?*
- ▶ *Which number has the most hundreds beads? Which has the fewest?*
- ▶ *Write the numbers in order, from smallest to largest.*
- ▶ *Which number has the most beads altogether? Which has the fewest?*

108 A **game for three or four players**, using two sets of 0–9 number cards, counters, a pile of interlocking cubes and copies of pcm 40. Each player needs a copy of the pcm and counters. The number cards are shuffled and one is dealt to each player. This number represents each player's units, and a matching number of counters are placed on each player's abacus. The cards are dealt again, the number this time representing tens, and again for hundreds – players placing matching numbers of counters on their abacus. Then each player places their number cards underneath the abacus to represent the three-digit number shown. They say their numbers in turn. The players with most counters in the hundreds position and in the tens and units positions all collect a cube. So does the player who has placed most counters altogether. Play continues for several rounds. The first player to collect ten cubes wins. [P] [G]

109 The children use three counters on the abacus on pcm 40. [P] [G]
Ask them:
- ▶ *How many different numbers can be created with the three counters?*
- ▶ *How many are one-digit numbers, how many are two-digit numbers and how many are three-digit numbers?*

They extend the activity to using four, then five counters.
Note A spike abacus and beads can be used to help with this activity.

Answers

107 The beads for each number are:

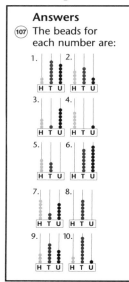

Smallest number 8. 60, largest: 7. 625.
Most units beads: 6. 78, fewest units beads: 5. 430 and 8. 60.
Most tens beads: 10. 281, fewest tens beads: 4. 501.
Most hundreds beads: 7. 625, Fewest hundreds beads: 6. 78. and 8. 60.
Numbers in order are: 60,78,276,281,316,364, 430,452,501,625.
Most beads altogether: 1. 276 (15),
fewest beads altogether 4. 501 and 8. 60 (6).

With three counters, ten different numbers are possible. They are:
one-digit number: 3;
two-digit numbers: 12, 21, 30;
three-digit numbers: 102, 111,120, 201, 210, 300.

With four counters, 15 different numbers are possible. They are:
one-digit number: 4;
two-digit numbers: 13, 22, 31, 40;
three-digit numbers: 103, 112, 121, 130, 202, 211, 220, 301, 310, 400.

With five counters, 21 different numbers are possible. They are:
one-digit number: 5;
two-digit numbers: 14, 23, 32, 41, 50;
three-digit numbers: 104, 113, 122, 131, 140, 203, 212, 221, 230, 302, 311, 320, 401, 410, 500.

You need spike abacus and beads (optional)

Abacus beads

▶ **Write the numbers shown by these beads.**

1.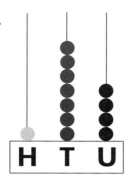
H T U
___

2.
H T U
___

3.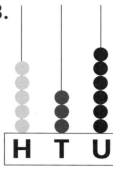
H T U
___

4.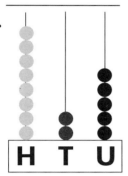
H T U
___

5.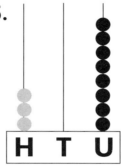
H T U
___

6.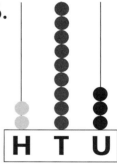
H T U
___

▶ **Draw beads on each abacus to show these numbers.**

7.
H T U
1 5 6

8.
H T U
2 7 3

9.
H T U
4 0 5

10.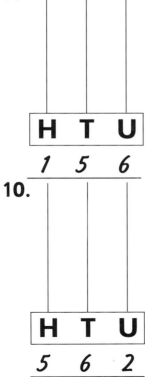
H T U
5 6 2

11.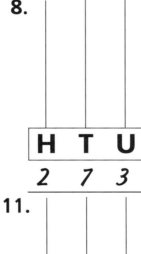
H T U
3 3 0

12.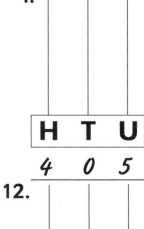
H T U
6 4 7

Name .... Date ....

Abacus

► **Place counters on the abacus to show these numbers:**

1. 276   2. 452   3. 316   4. 501   5. 430

6. 78   7. 625   8. 60   9. 364   10. 281.

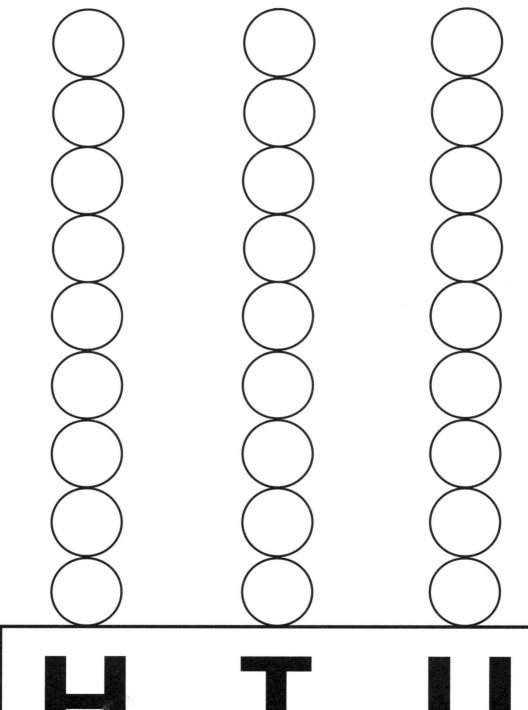

| H | T | U |

Name .... Date ....

100 IDEAS for MATHS 5 –7 © HarperCollins*Publishers* Ltd 1996